Hard Questions about Health and Healing

Dr Andrew Fergusson

Contents

Acknowledgements

I would like to thank:

- Christian Medical Fellowship, all the members of its Publications Committee, Rachael Pickering, Giles Rawlinson, Peter Saunders, Allister Vale and especially the late John Alford, who began work on final design and production but sadly did not live to see the book come to fruition;
- medical colleagues and fellow members of CMF, especially Peter May and Trevor Stammers with whom I held many discussions about healing in the early 1990s;
- colleagues in the Acorn Christian Foundation, especially Roy Lawrence, Michael Mitton and Russ Parker whose teaching, writing and practice have been an inspiration;
- my wife, family, and many Christian friends at church and elsewhere who prayed for this book.

Christian Medical Fellowship has well over 4,000 British doctors in all branches of the profession and 1,000 medical students as members. It seeks to relate Christianity into the medical world, and in partnership with others has a growing influence nationally and internationally.

For general enquiries contact:

Christian Medical Fellowship
157 Waterloo Road, London. SE1 8XN
Tel 020 7928 4694; Fax 020 7620 2453
Email info@cmf.org.uk; *Website* www.cmf.org.uk

Forewords

Health is an issue that everyone is concerned about. It seems that we have come to expect perfect health, and are less willing to accept any form of disease or disability. Yet what do we mean by health? Can anyone be totally healthy and do we have the right to expect this for ourselves?

In my work as a paediatrician caring for extremely premature babies and their families, my colleagues and I are frequently brought face to face with the pain of suffering, and death. The question parents often ask is, 'Why has this happened to us?' It's one of many hard questions that health professionals and carers can't get away from. We need a solid framework to think about these hard questions and I am convinced that the historic Christian faith provides such a basis for our thinking and caring. It is this faith that teaches us about the wonder and the shame of being human, and about the God who enters into our experience and shares it with us.

Andrew Fergusson's unique experience – both in primary care medicine and as a leader in the Christian Medical Fellowship – equips him to tackle the fundamental questions underlining our modern health-orientated culture. What is health? Can we be healthy even in the presence of physical disease? Do suffering and disability have any positive sides, both for the individual and for society at large? What is healing, how can it be obtained and when is it enough?

Christian doctors and other health professionals are in a unique and privileged position. Alongside physical treatments, they can offer hope, spiritual wholeness and a realistic vision of health in a world that is both wonderful yet fundamentally flawed. They can embody the presence of Christ in the midst of suffering. And in the radical combination of practical caring and Christian hope they can point beyond disease, physical degeneration and death, to the renewal of all things, when: 'There will be no more death or mourning or crying or pain, for the old order of things has passed away' (Revelation 21:4).

John Wyatt
Professor of Neonatology, University College Hospital London
Chairman, Medical Study Group, Christian Medical Fellowship
December 2004

I am so glad that this book has been written. It provides three necessary links of understanding – bridge, border and boundary – between health professionals and the Christian prayer approach to healing.

It is a bridge in that it offers insights into legitimate collaboration between Christian faith and professional skills within healthcare settings. Andrew illuminates this with insights from his time as a Christian GP; I found them a most appealing and powerful aspect of the book.

Andrew explores the border country, where opportunities to introduce a specific Christian presence into the medical world remain open to us. What it means to be human and how it affects the focus and delivery of care is of crucial importance. The recent NHS focus on spirituality offers an open door for Christian responses such as Andrew's book. Andrew and I have travelled widely as part of our work for the Acorn Christian Foundation, facilitating meetings between health care professionals and practitioners of prayer for healing. Helping them share insights and resources has been an exhilarating and rewarding experience, a vision of the possibilities to renew and restore a Christian presence within hospitals and surgeries alike.

This book is also a boundary that encourages us to honour and respect each other's engagement in care, health and healing. Not infrequently have I paused when preaching to apologise to health professionals for the times those involved in the church healing ministry have demeaned their importance in healthcare delivery. There is a great need to appreciate the differences that lie between professionals and those who pray for healing in a church setting.

Sooner or later, all those involved in health and healing have to answer a range of difficult questions. 'What should we expect from our labours? What do we say to those who look to us for their healing? What if it doesn't work?' Andrew's book helps us tackle difficult issues, looking honestly at our questions and doubts. Our involvement in Christ's care of others will be all the richer and more rewarding if we stay open to such challenges. I welcome this book as a fresh look at healing, and hope that it will strengthen your faith and renew your medical practice.

The Rev Dr Russ Parker
Director, Acorn Christian Foundation
December 2004

Preface

There are many Christian books on the market about healing but most are from a lay perspective, written by Christians in churches for Christians in churches. There is little from a medical perspective on Christian views of health and healing, and indeed the two constituencies of the health professional (who may be a Christian) and the Christian who prays for healing rarely meet. This book attempts to bridge that gap.

This is a book by a doctor for doctors and other health professionals. I have worked for nearly 14 years in clinical medicine, and have since been at the interface of medical practice and Christianity; I write for fellow health professionals who may be Christians. I hope in addition that many who are not yet Christians and many Christians with a lay interest in health and healing will read it with benefit. I have written primarily with a UK readership in mind but there are principles that apply anywhere in the world.

I attempt to set out the way Christian health professionals think through aspects of health and healing. This is important because what we think determines what we do. Every country of the world is uncertain about the way ahead for healthcare, particularly with regard to resources. I hope this book will contribute to the best use of resources and will benefit the health of individuals and populations.

Andrew Fergusson
December 2004

What is the Christian worldview?

Where is she now?

Three young doctors meet up in the pub after attending the funeral service and cremation of one of their colleagues. She died in a single vehicle accident, driving home at dawn after a night on duty in Accident and Emergency.

'She fell asleep. She was shattered. We shouldn't have to work such hours,' says one.

'Sure it wasn't suicide?' asks another. 'They say single vehicle accidents are nearly always suicide'.

The third colleague: 'Who knows? And who cares? What matters is she's gone, and it's all such a waste!'

There is silence for a while.

'I wonder where she is now?'

'I'll tell you where she is,' comes a reply. 'She's ash in the incinerator. That's all. When you're dead, you're dead. It's all over.'

'Oh no,' the questioner responds. 'She'll be reincarnated, and she'll probably have a better deal next time round…though I wonder if this happened because of a bad life last time?'

'That's rubbish! Physical laws of the universe were broken; the car crashed; she's dead. End of story. End of the only story.'

Threatened, the doctor who has been challenged turns to their colleague. 'No, it can't be the end. What do you think? You're religious too, aren't you?'

'I don't understand it, but I don't think this caught God out. Somehow it makes sense to Him. And somehow she continues to exist somewhere…either in heaven or…' and he broke off with a worried look on his face.

'Oh, forget it. These questions are too hard.'

And they drink more deeply.

What are worldviews?

Each of us has a worldview whether we realise it or not, and there are three different worldviews in these doctors' comments. Worldviews are the frameworks we hold for understanding how the world works, for explaining it to ourselves, and for understanding what our own part is in the world. This book is explicitly Christian, so I will begin by explaining briefly what Christians believe and introduce some of the concepts and language that will occur throughout the book. I will use as little jargon as possible and, at the risk of patronising some or all, will start by assuming nothing.

What do Christians believe?

This is not a particularly hard question but answering it simply and briefly may be harder. Let me begin with the sort of introduction I might use in discussion with an individual or a group:

'The whole of the Christian worldview can be reduced to five simple propositions.

God

'The first proposition is about the existence of God. He is one absolute, eternal, personal, spiritual being who has made the world and everything in it, including you and me. There are several ways we know about God but the most reliable is through the Christian claim that God has taken human form and lived on earth in the person of his only son, the historic human being Jesus Christ.

'The famous Christian writer C S Lewis used the analogy of Shakespeare and Hamlet. Shakespeare was a playwright and Hamlet is the lead character in a play of that name. Lewis argued that there was no way Hamlet could ever have met Shakespeare, but there was a way in which Shakespeare could have met Hamlet. Shakespeare could have written himself into the plot of *Hamlet* so that there, on the stage, maybe in Act 3 Scene 2 , he, the playwright, the creator, could have met his creation, Hamlet. Christians believe that God has written himself directly into the plot of human history in the person of his son, Jesus Christ. '

Man and woman

'Secondly we need to consider the nature of human beings. We are all made in the image of God (see chapter two for an explanation of the significance of this image) and are meant to have a relationship with him. However, it is in our nature to do wrong sometimes and by the wrong choices each of us makes we cut ourselves off from God and our relationship with him; hence our relationships with other people and the environment are spoiled.'

God

'We come back to God again. God is love and wants the best for us, so he has to resolve this problem we have created. He sends his son to earth to show us how to live, to teach, to perform miracles, but ultimately he sends him to die on the cross. In this way, the penalty a holy and just God requires for our wrong choices can be met.'

What if I do?

'The fourth proposition concerns a positive response from an individual. If I respond by turning away from the wrong way of living, by thanking God that the penalty for my wrong choices has been met by Christ's death on the cross, by acknowledging that God has confirmed his power in raising Jesus from the dead, and by committing myself from now on to living for Christ, then I know a new life.

'I know new life here on earth, both naturally through the deep sense of peace that comes from realising God's forgiveness, and supernaturally through God's presence as he comes to live within me through his Holy Spirit. I will know that new life in heaven and can be certain of being with God eternally when I die, not because of what I have done but because of my faith in what Jesus has done.'

What if I don't?

'Finally, what happens to the individual who responds negatively? If I ignore God, either passively and apathetically, or in active rebellion and rejection, then by my own choice I will not know that new life now on earth either naturally or supernaturally. If I continue to ignore God up to the end of my life then one day God will have to say, "I'm sorry, I don't know you. You didn't want to know me. I can't let you into my heaven". I will forever be separated from God in hell.'

These five propositions sum up the entire Christian message and it can therefore be presented very succinctly. However my experience is that, if the listener has taken all five points on board, the conversation is unlikely to stop there!

What are the seven deadly questions?

When a presentation like this is made to twenty-first century health professionals, then in the ensuing discussion certain questions inevitably follow:

1. Is Christ the only way to God?
2. Isn't the Bible full of errors?
3. Isn't Christian experience only psychological?
4. How can miracles be possible?
5. What about those who have never heard the gospel?
6. Why do the innocent suffer?
7. Won't a good moral life get me to heaven?

Note that the questions are limited in number. Although there may be a few more than seven, or they may be expressed in somewhat different terms, these others are just variations on a theme. The specific objections are finite and few. Secondly, while the questions may superficially appear lethal to the Christian case, there are in fact good answers readily available. This book will only touch specifically on the questions about miracles and about suffering, but answers to the others can be found elsewhere (see *References and Further Reading* at the end of the chapter).

How can God have a Son, and who is the Holy Spirit?

I will not attempt in this short chapter to cover all the issues of Christian theology that arise from the five propositions summary, but this book is about health, healing, and healthcare. These issues involve people and their relationships so I will pause to emphasise that God himself exists in three persons who are in relationship with each other. A Bible verse often used in Christian worship as *The Grace* reads, 'May the grace of the Lord Jesus Christ, and the love of God, and the fellowship of the Holy Spirit be with you all' (2 Corinthians 13:14). God the Father, God the Son and God the Holy Spirit are explicitly mentioned together in this blessing. As Reginald Heber's classic hymn puts it, Christians worship 'God in three Persons, blessèd Trinity'. How can this be?

The first thing to say is that we cannot understand this fully. Indeed, there is much concerning Christianity that we cannot understand fully, but in medicine that problem never seems to stop us practising! We do the best we can with the information available, and so it is with Christianity. The following two analogies have helped me to understand how one God can exist in three Persons.

Firstly, think of the chemical formula H_2O. According to the temperature, that one chemical formula can exist in three different physical forms: ice, water or steam. The molecule is fundamentally the same one but may exist in three different forms. I once knew enough physics both to understand and accept that. I've now forgotten my physics but I still accept that this is the way H_2O is. Similarly, God is fundamentally the one God but he exists in three different forms.

Another analogy that may be helpful is to think of any one individual but then to consider their different relationships. For example, I am the father of my son and daughter; at the same time I am the son of my late father; and also at the same time I am the husband of my wife. There's only one of me but I am father, son and husband.

Neither of these illustrations is more than an analogy, but I have found them both of some help in understanding how God exists as Father, Son and Holy Spirit.

Shouldn't everything we practise be evidence-based?

Quite rightly, Western medical practice is evidence-based as far as possible. It may be tempting to reject consideration of everything to do with Christianity, religion and spirituality as, by definition, not being amenable to evidence-based assessment.

However, the reliability of the documents making up the Bible can be assessed. The facts of Jesus' life and death are open to historical analysis. The questions of the empty tomb and whether Jesus has in fact been raised from the dead are open to logical analysis: it makes a great detective story and, medicine being very similar to criminal detection, a great diagnostic challenge.

Of course, medicine is not an exact science. History, examination and special tests take us to the most likely diagnosis but we are never 100·00% sure. At the end of the day, there is always a small element of faith in each diagnosis and its management. So it is with Christianity. I became a Christian half way through my six years at medical school, overwhelmed by the weight of the evidence and attracted by the evidence of the life of Christ in the lives of certain friends. They had something I did not have and I wanted it. But I was not 100·00% sure when, in the end by faith, I made a commitment to Christ. That commitment has changed my life for more than 30 years and I am now as close to 100·00% sure as makes no difference.

God will honour you if you genuinely wrestle with the evidence. I cannot prove to you the truth of the five propositions outlined above, but you can prove them for yourself.

What is the Bible?

Christians believe God has revealed himself in writing and that the Holy Bible is a library of 66 books that records all we need to know of God's dealing with men and women. The books fit into different sections of the library (history, law, poetry, wisdom literature, prophecy and letters) and therefore need to be interpreted accordingly; yet, the Bible is true and reliable.

In the healing miracles we will consider in chapter five, the accounts of Jesus healing people are factually true. The miracles actually happened. They are, quite simply, history. The Bible literally means what it says with regard to these accounts. When we come to consider whether we should be expecting such miracles today, we need to look at different passages of the Bible and apply them. Because they come from different kinds of writing, from different sections of the library of 66 books, we need to exercise a degree of interpretation. We are quite entitled to apply the wisdom and the logic God has given us, and that is part of what we mean by interpretation.

But we must interpret the Bible consistently. There are certain great themes within it; to avoid the temptation to be selective, cherry picking some verses while ignoring others that don't suit our presuppositions, we need a scheme for ensuring a safe and comprehensive analysis. I make no claims to be a theologian myself. Quoting from the five propositions above, I find it helpful to use the following four great theological pillars:

> **Creation** – 'God...has made the world and everything in it, including you and me.'
> **Fall** – '...it is in our nature to do wrong sometimes and by the wrong choices each of us makes we cut ourselves off from God and our relationship with him; hence our relationships with other people and the environment are spoiled.'
> **Redemption** – 'If I respond by turning away from the wrong way of living, by thanking God that the penalty for my wrong choices has been met by Christ's death on the cross, by acknowledging that God has confirmed his power in raising Jesus from the dead, and by committing myself from now on to living for Christ, then I know a new life.'
> **Future hope** – 'I will know that new life in heaven and can be certain of being with God eternally when I die, not

because of what I have done but because of my faith in what Jesus has done.'

I give these four theological pillars tabloid style subtitles:

Creation – *how was it?*
Fall – *how is it?*
Redemption – *how could/should it be?*
Future hope – *how will it be?*

Several subsequent chapters, for example chapter two, *What does it mean to be human?* and chapter five, *What does the Bible say?* will follow this scheme.

How can scientifically trained doctors possibly be Christians?

It has been said that God has revealed himself in two books. One is the Bible, which we have just been considering as a true and reliable guide to everything God wants to say to us. The other is the book of his creation, the book of nature. We can study this book and investigate the world by scientific enquiry and research.

There is a famous aphorism: 'Scientific research is thinking God's thoughts after him'. I have seen this attributed both to Sir Isaac Newton and to the astronomer, Kepler. It is an awe-inspiring statement.

Back in the early 1970s, while doing an intercalated degree in human physiology as part of my medical training, I spent part of a summer vacation doing some research with a senior colleague into the control of the secretion of a particular hormone. We were privileged to make a modest breakthrough. For a while, we were the only two people on earth, as far as we knew, who were aware of the new facts we had discovered. Of course, it was soon published in the appropriate journal and knowledge about that particular subject has moved on many times since then. But I was awed by what we found out. I got a real buzz out of it. Yet it wasn't the buzz that would have been usual for me at that time, a sort of 'Look at me! I'm wonderful!' Instead there was a buzz, 'That's incredible! That can't have come about randomly by chance. There must be design'.

Though I certainly didn't know it at the time, we were thinking God's thoughts after him. This happened to me just before I began considering the claims of Christianity seriously. Looking back, I think it was all part of the process of my becoming a Christian; by that, I mean the process of my coming to have a new relationship with God, coming to hold the Christian worldview, and coming to live my life accordingly.

Science cannot disprove God. The word *science* simply means knowledge: it is the sum of what we know from studying the other book. By its nature, science cannot give us the tools to disprove the existence of God. How, for example, do you measure God's love? Christians should always encourage the scientific methodology of using logic to set up and test hypotheses, and use the technology science has given us when it is appropriate to do so; yet, science is ultimately a tool with limited application. Just as we wouldn't use a CT or MRI scan for an examination for which they were not indicated, or even contraindicated, so we shouldn't try to use science to examine the claim, *God is love.*

Many contemporary doctors and scientists around the world are committed Christians. There is no fundamental incompatibility between Christianity and scientific medicine.

References and Further Reading

Confident Christianity. London: Christian Medical Fellowship, 2000.
A series of articles (including a page on each of the seven deadly questions) that can be viewed on the CMF website www.cmf.org.uk or is obtainable in A4 booklet form from 157 Waterloo Road, London. SE1 8XN

May P. *The Greatest Person?* London: Christian Medical Fellowship, 1996.
This introduction to Jesus Christ can also be viewed on the CMF website www.cmf.org.uk or is obtainable in A6 booklet form from 157 Waterloo Road, London. SE1 8XN

2

What does it mean to be human?

In 1997, I was sitting in the CMF office when news broke of the birth of Dolly the sheep. This first cloned mammal led to much media speculation about the possibility of cloning a human being; for several weeks I was bombarded with phone calls from the very bright young people who dominate the media. Implicit or explicit in their questioning was 'What does it mean to be human?'

In terms of the ethical debate, the cloning of a human being sadly looks more likely now than it did then; although, in terms of the scientific issues involved, successful human cloning looks less likely. But the question 'What does it mean to be human?' is being asked as much now as it was then and it is a vital question for anyone concerned with healthcare.

We introduced this subject in the first chapter. Now we will look in detail at what the Bible has to say and then compare that with the intuitions we all hold.

What does the Bible say?

I will follow the four pillars approach outlined in chapter one:

1. Creation – how was it?

We need to start at the very beginning of the Bible, in the book of Genesis, the book of beginnings. The very first words of the Bible are 'In the beginning God...' It may well be intellectually frustrating that there is so much built into those four majestic words; we may share the curiosity of the small child who asks, 'But who was God's mummy?' Yet those words are where we have to start. We cannot go behind them.

The account continues: 'In the beginning God created the heavens and the earth' and then runs on through the creation of light and darkness; water and sky; land and sea; vegetation; sun, moon and stars; sea creatures and birds; livestock and wild animals. At intervals we read, *'And God saw that it was good'*.

Of course, there is a great debate about all this. The Bible uses the language of 'God created' but since the days of Darwin there has been much excited consideration of the process of evolution. The 19th century church reacted badly to Darwin's theory and there has been an artificial and in my view largely unnecessary debate going on ever since. This debate is artificial because we are failing to recognise the relative roles and responsibilities of the two books I mentioned in chapter one. Genesis tells us *who* did *what* and a little about *why*. It does not tell us about *when, where* and *how*. For that we need to examine the other book of nature.

I am married to an anthropologist but I am afraid that I still find everything to do with fossils incredibly boring! The evolution debate is about the *when, where* and *how* and for that you will have to look elsewhere. Genesis gives us an overview, an outline account of *who* did *what*; towards the end of chapter one, in verses 26-28, we read:

> *Then God said, "Let us make man in our image, in our likeness, and let them rule over the fish of the sea and the birds of the air, over the livestock, over all the earth, and over all the creatures that move along the ground." So God created man in his own image, in the image of God he created him; male and female he created them. God blessed them and said to them, "Be fruitful and increase in number; fill the earth and subdue it. Rule over the fish of the sea and the birds of the air and over every living creature that moves on the ground."*

It is worth noting that God uses the language 'Let us make' and 'in our image'. The language is plural, and a legitimate ultimate reference here is to the Trinity. In chapter one we saw how, although there is one God, he is in three persons: Father, Son and Holy Spirit. God is in relationship with himself within the persons of what is called the Godhead, and this motif of relationship runs throughout the Bible as it runs throughout the obligations of healthcare.

Secondly, whenever God says he will do something, he does it. It may be done sooner or later, but God keeps his word. It is worth bearing that principle of the character of God in mind when we come to consider the (relatively few) promises that have not yet been fulfilled.

Thirdly, it is only after he has completed all his work with the creation of man and woman that we read God's commendation upgraded: 'God saw all that he had made, and it was very good' (Genesis 1:31).

What does 'in the image of God' mean?

The central message in Genesis 1:26-28 is that, unlike the animals, man and woman are made 'in the image of God'. This is an enormously important idea for the practice of healthcare. How are we to understand it?

First, we can think about the metaphor of image. There are really three ideas:

- **Relationship** – image implies face-to-face relationship. God wants to have a face-to-face relationship with us.
- **Reflection** – most of us think of images in terms of reflections in mirrors. The image I see in the shaving mirror is the reverse of what others see of me. God made us to reflect himself: it is his intention that people should see something of God when they look at us. Do we reflect God to others?
- **Representation** – if the image on a coin is to represent the rule of the monarch or statesman so pictured, how far do we represent God on earth?

We will see below that, because of the second theological pillar of the Fall, relationship with God is broken and reflection and representation are not as true as they should be; because of the third pillar of redemption, they can at least partially become restored. In my first chapter, I said that as important as the weight of the evidence in my becoming a Christian was the fact that I could see evidence of the life of Jesus Christ in the lives of some of my fellow students, but not in others and certainly not in my own life. Those few had something and I wanted it.

Having introduced this concept of image, the Bible doesn't define it. Yet, the importance of the concept is underlined a few chapters further on in the prescription of capital punishment for murder:

> *And from each man, too, I will demand an accounting for the life of his fellow man. Whoever sheds the blood of man, by man shall his blood be shed; for in the image of God has God made man. (Genesis 9:5-6)*

God so values human life because it is made in his image and is intended to represent him on earth. He so values it that, almost paradoxically, he prescribes the death penalty for murder. The relevance of the concepts in this text for the capital punishment, abortion and euthanasia debates cannot be considered here; at the very least, we can see that God takes image very seriously.

What more do we learn in Genesis chapter two?

The second chapter of Genesis is a complementary account of the creation. The skeleton is fleshed out, particularly with regard to man and woman. Unlike the animals, human beings are made in the image of God; so, we are:

- **Immortal** '...you must not eat from the tree of the knowledge of good and evil, for when you eat of it you will surely die' (Genesis 2:17). Immortality is a difficult concept to understand. This quote only introduces it in a roundabout way but it is more than wishful thinking. Death is not the end for human beings. Something of us continues forever, eternally, and that is true irrespective of whether we believe it or not. The only question is where we are going to spend eternity, in heaven or in hell.

- **Spiritual** 'And the Lord God . . . breathed into his nostrils the breath of life' (Genesis 2:7). For hundreds of years, Western medicine ignored the spiritual aspect of man and – as they said, if it exists – let the church have it. However, over the last couple of decades the spiritual is firmly back on the healthcare agenda. I will consider what is meant by spiritual below and much of the rest of this book will deal with it.

- **Creative** '...whatever the man called each living creature, that was its name' (Genesis 2:19). The first specific job man was given in the Garden of Eden was to name the animals. When we name something, we have an immense responsibility and may do much to determine outcomes. Imagine Adam starting with *aardvark* and working on through to *zebra*. My tongue may be slightly in my cheek there. When my wife and I were expecting our children, we put a great deal of thought and prayer into the meanings of the names we chose for them. Of course, being creative goes far beyond choosing names. Think of art, literature, music, interior design, gardening or even surgery. Unlike an ant programmed to make a nest or a beaver constructing a dam, human beings are creative like God himself, for the sake of beauty as well as function.

- **Created for relationships** 'The Lord God said, "It is not good for the man to be alone. I will make a helper suitable for him"' (Genesis 2:18). This text goes on to describe the first general anaesthetic and surgical operation in history: 'So the Lord God caused the man to fall into a deep sleep; and while he was sleeping, he took one of the man's ribs and closed up the place with flesh. Then the Lord God made a woman from the rib he had taken out of the man, and he brought her to the man'. This is trying to teach us that man and woman are complementary. Amongst other things, the length of the description underscores God's knowledge of our need for relationship. Nowhere is that relationship more developed than in marriage.

- **Created with capacity for moral choices** 'And the Lord God commanded the man, "You are free to eat from any tree in the garden; but you must not eat from the tree of the knowledge of good and evil..."' (Genesis 2:16-17). Man is given one prohibition, presented with that one moral choice. Like God himself, we have the capacity for moral choices. We are ethical beings.

Whilst physically we have much in common with animals, the Bible tells us that we are qualitatively different from them because of the image of God. We are a quantum leap different from them. Although there are many similarities, doctors and veterinary surgeons are working with very different material.

This was vividly brought home to me some years ago when the Voluntary Euthanasia Society invited me to speak as an opponent at their Annual General Meeting. They tolerated my hard-hitting critique quite politely until I used the expression, 'We are not animals'. This started up several minutes of shouts and cries. The hall was filled with such noises that they appeared to be proving their point. The chairman took his time restoring order. To an extent the audience was right: I should more accurately have said, 'We are not just animals'. But the difference in our worldviews regarding what it meant to be human was responsible for our diametrically opposed views on the ethics of euthanasia.

What does the Old Testament say about holism?

The Lord God formed man from the dust of the ground and breathed into his nostrils the breath of life, and man became a living being. (Genesis 2:7)

This single verse in the second chapter of Genesis tells us that each and every human being is an indivisible whole of body, soul or mind, and spirit (or an indivisible whole of body and soul) where the whole is more than the sum of the parts.

By far the most important point here is that the Bible emphasises that man is a unity created by God. Clearly, there is a difference between the physical and the non-physical. Yet theologians then debate whether man is in two parts (body and soul) or three (body, soul or mind, and spirit) – see *References and Further Reading* at the end of the chapter.

These arguments are too many and complex for this basic book but I am personally persuaded by the dichotomy of body and soul rather than the trichotomy of body, soul or mind, and spirit. However, the important number is not the *two* of dichotomy or the *three* of trichotomy but the *one* of unity!

Body and soul is still a familiar figure of speech in everyday language, as in 'keeping body and soul together', and there is advantage in using the language our patients use. As a non-theologian, I suspect that it does not matter very much in practical terms. Are we not really trying to differentiate the spiritual from the material, the eternal aspect of human beings from the temporal, the immortal from that which will one day die? Are we not trying to differentiate the tent from the person who camps in that tent for a while?

Genesis 2:7 has three elements in it so let us examine each of these in turn:

- **Body** *'The Lord God formed the man from the dust of the ground...'*
  It is obvious from our studies in early embryology through to the post mortem room, from biochemistry through to brain surgery, that human beings have much in common biologically with the other parts of God's creation. 50 percent of our DNA is identical to the DNA of a cabbage. More than 98 percent of our DNA is identical to the DNA of a chimpanzee. Does that mean the 'image of God' is located somewhere in the other two percent? No! To think like that would be to confuse categories. We have much in common with other parts of creation; remembering that God placed us at the pinnacle of creation, it should not surprise us at all that many of the building bricks he used are common.

  Because of this commonality, a great deal of progress has been made in medical research through studying both lower and higher animals. Provided those creatures are treated with respect, they can be used legitimately and within limits in experimentation. This respect must reflect the responsibility God has given us for the whole of creation. We have already seen Genesis 1:28: '...fill the earth and subdue it. Rule over the fish of the sea and the birds of the air and over every living creature that moves on the ground'.

  Subduing and ruling are words describing our responsibility to look after the earth and everything and everyone on it, and to be accountable for what we do. We must care for creation as

God would, not by domination or exploitation. We have a mandate to be stewards of the earth, stewards of health and healing.

Medical studies give us a privileged insight into the intricacy of the human body; in chapter one, I described the buzz I got from a piece of research. The Book of Psalms in the Bible contains poems, often set to music, and I am in a position to agree with David, a King of Israel: 'I praise you because I am fearfully and wonderfully made; your works are wonderful, I know that full well' (Psalm 139:14).

• **Spirit** '*...and breathed into his nostrils the breath of life...*'

God has breathed spirituality into each and every one of us. In his Commentary on Genesis, Derek Kidner notes that the two verbs formed and breathed balance: '*Formed* expresses the relation of craftsman to material...while *breathed* is warmly personal, with the face-to-face intimacy of a kiss and the significance that this was an act of giving as well as making; and self-giving at that'.

Nowadays we all know what spirituality is but it can be hard to pin down into words. Collins English Dictionary (21st Century Edition, 2000) is not particularly helpful in its definition: 'relating to the spirit or soul and not to physical nature or matter; intangible'. There are other theoretical definitions of spirituality but I prefer a practical definition around the 'Why?' questions. Examples of such questions our patients ask include, 'Why pain? Why suffering? Why me? Why now?'

Ian Ainsworth Smith, the Chaplain at St George's Hospital in London, defines spirituality as 'that which human beings use to hold their past, their present and their future in meaningful continuity'.

Until quite recently, Western medicine would have given no consideration at all to spiritual issues, but now they are officially back on the government's healthcare agenda. This is a tremendous opportunity for Christian health professionals.

• **Soul or Mind** '*...and man became a living being.*'

After God has formed the man from the dust of the ground, as a master potter working with clay, and after he has breathed into man's nostrils the breath of life, we read that man becomes a 'living being'. Here we have the totality of intellect, personality and attributes that makes each and every one of us unique and readily recognisable. Living being perhaps doesn't fully do justice to all that is encompassed.

Therefore, the picture of human beings we have from this first theological pillar, Creation, is that we are made in the image of God and that we are an indivisible whole of body plus mind plus spirit (or body and soul) where the whole is greater than the sum of the parts. I keep using the concept of whole: from this we get the now commonplace ideas of holism and holistic health.

Does the New Testament view humans holistically?

The New Testament is the second part of the Bible. The books in it deal with the life of Christ and the early years afterwards. It confirms that the biblical view of human beings is holistic.

Luke is one of the four Gospel writers. It is interesting that, as a doctor, he alone gives us this picture of paediatric development in his description of the boy Jesus: 'And the child grew and became strong; he was filled with wisdom, and the grace of God was upon him' (Luke 2: 40). We read of the physical aspect of Christ in '...grew and became strong...'; of the mental in '...he was filled with wisdom...'; and of the spiritual in '...the grace of God was upon him'.

In his first letter to the Thessalonians, the apostle Paul is sending a blessing to Christians in Thessalonika and reminding them that Jesus is coming back (one of those promises I mentioned earlier that is yet to be fulfilled): 'May God himself, the God of peace, sanctify you through and through. May your whole spirit, soul and body be kept blameless at the coming of our Lord Jesus Christ' (1 Thessalonians 5:23). Paul is really emphasising 'through and through' with reference to the three aspects of human being. He is really saying, 'every part of you'.

What is dualism and why is it dangerous?

The biblical picture of what it means to be human, from Genesis, the book of beginnings, in the Old Testament, and the New Testament, is that we are an indivisible whole. We are souls and we are bodies. We are neither bodies that have souls nor, though this is nearer the truth, souls who have bodies. The Greek idea of dualism grew up after Plato (c428-348 BC): it saw the body as a material container that held the immaterial soul for a while. Dualism caused a great debate over the point at which the soul entered the body, and the point at which it left. A Victorian philanthropist offered a huge cash prize for anyone who could convincingly photograph the soul leaving the body – I understand the money hasn't been claimed yet! Much more recently, a British Law Lord said of Tony Bland, a young man in a permanent vegetative state: 'His spirit has left him and all that remains is the shell of his body'. Even by British judicial standards of omniscience, that is an astonishingly presumptuous pronouncement!

This idea of dualism is dangerous for medical ethics. If there was a time before an embryo or a foetus had a soul, then experimentation on the embryo and abortion of the foetus might perhaps be more likely to be ethically permissible. If people in permanent vegetative states really are shells that have been vacated by their spirits, then the ethics of the decision about withdrawing tube feeding might be easier. But we are *not* bodies that have souls, nor souls who have bodies. We are bodies *and* we are souls. Using a biblical metaphor that is a favourite of mine, the person matters more than the tent they inhabit, but that tent matters here on earth while we need it.

So why are we still on the first pillar?

Much the greatest part of this chapter concentrates on the first pillar, Creation, because an understanding of how God made us in the beginning should give us an insight into how God intended things to be. And I have one final point. What God says is best regarding the care of the human body and soul is true both for the patient who holds the Christian faith and for the patient who does not yet hold it. Why? Because we are all made the same way.

When I am teaching about this, I use an example from my do-it-yourself days. I describe a typical self-assembly disaster and then ask the audience why I am the only one who knows how the fitment I have just put together really works. After a while, I get the answer, 'Because you made it'. Those four words are so profound for the whole of our healthcare. God knows best what is needed for the body and soul of each and every one of us because he made us. That is why this first pillar of Creation is so important.

2. Fall – how is it?

Our second pillar has the short but complicated theological title of The Fall. As we have seen, the first and second chapters of Genesis describe the perfect world of Eden that God made and gave to Adam and Eve to enjoy, reproduce in, and fill. Chapter three follows chapters one and two: enter the serpent who '...was more crafty than any of the wild animals the Lord God had made' (Genesis 3:1). A symbol of evil, he tempts first Eve and then Adam to disobey God's one and only prohibition: 'And the Lord God commanded the man, "You are free to eat from any tree in the garden; but you must not eat from the tree of the knowledge of good and evil, for when you eat of it you will surely die."' (Genesis 2:16-17)

Adam and Eve's mistakes are typical of all sins since, of all mine and of all yours. The essence of all sin is putting human judgment above divine command. Actions have consequences and the long-term effects of sin start to appear. The serpent is judged; for woman, the world of the womb is cursed: 'To the woman he said, "I will greatly increase your pains in childbearing; with pain you will give birth to children. Your desire will be for your husband, and he will rule over you."' (Genesis 3:16)

For man the world of work is cursed: 'To Adam he said, "Because you listened to your wife and ate from the tree about which I commanded you, 'You must not eat of it,' "Cursed is the ground because of you; through painful toil you will eat of it all the days of your life. It will produce thorns and thistles for you, and you will eat the plants of the field. By the sweat of your brow you will eat your food until you return to the ground, since from it you were taken; for dust you are and to dust you will return."' (Genesis 3:17-19)

At the end of Genesis chapter three, Adam and Eve are expelled from the garden and the extent of the serpent's lie in verse four – 'You will not surely die…' – now becomes clear. They continue to have some sort of life outside the garden but it is a mere shadow of what they had enjoyed before. They no longer enjoy intimate fellowship with God himself; they no longer enjoy each other in the same way; and they now know pain and toil. Their relationships with God, the other, themselves, and their environment are all spoiled. The whole of creation comes under God's judgment; the effects on health through disease and dis-ease become obvious; and physical death arrives. New Testament verses commenting on these events state: '…sin entered the world through one man, and death through sin, and in this way death came to all men…' (Romans 5:12) and '…the wages of sin is death…' (Romans 6:23).

Sin has brought in its wake suffering and death. These are realities we all accept and expect, much as we would like to avoid them. They are here because of the Fall, that's the way it is. We will return to the Fall's effects in chapter 13, *Why does God allow suffering?*

This second theological pillar sets the context for consideration of health and healing. This is the world we live in.

3. Redemption – how could it be/how should it be?

Redemption is all about the difference made whenever anyone accepts by faith Jesus' death on the cross, and lives his or her life in God's new way thereafter. Jesus makes a difference. There are vivid examples of this in Paul's first letter to the church in Corinth. After listing a number of sexual and other sins, Paul says: 'And that is what some of you were. But you were washed, you were sanctified, you were justified in the name of the Lord Jesus Christ and by the Spirit of our God' (1 Corinthians 6:11).

Jesus makes a difference and so does the Holy Spirit. This is seen even more clearly when we contrast the acts of the sinful nature – 'sexual immorality, impurity and debauchery; idolatry and witchcraft; hatred, discord, jealousy, fits of rage, selfish ambition, dissensions, factions and envy; drunkenness, orgies and the like' – with 'But the fruit of the Spirit is love, joy, peace, patience, kindness, goodness, faithfulness, gentleness and self-control' (Galatians 5:19-23).

Redemption means being bought back. In times past, poor people facing a particular crisis of poverty would receive from a pawnbroker a sum of money far less than the item they handed over was worth. If they became flush with cash again, they could redeem the item by paying back a considerable amount more. The relevance to what Christ has done for us on the cross is clear: we had sold ourselves over to sin for far less than we were worth; God has bought us back at the considerably greater price of his son, Jesus.

The challenge to Christian health professionals facing any patient's problem is this: 'How can I bring Jesus into this situation?' And we must not underestimate the supernatural power potentially available. Whatever else it may be right to do, we can always pray, and we may then see interesting things happen (see chapter seven). Because God is in the business of redemption, until the moment of death there is always an earthly hope for health and healing.

4. Future hope – how will it be?

The fourth and final pillar relevant to health professionals regarding the question 'What does it mean to be human?' is future hope. Almost at the very end of the Bible, after hearing about 'a new heaven and a new earth' (Revelation 21:1), we read a detailed prophecy about heaven:

> *Now the dwelling of God is with men, and he will live with them. They will be his people, and God himself will be with them and be their God. He will wipe every tear from their eyes. There will be no more death or mourning or crying or pain, for the old order of things has passed away. (Revelation 21:3-4)*

Let me make clear right here that suffering is a bad thing and we should do everything legitimate we can to remove or reduce it. But we will never on this earth get rid of it all. If heaven is real, then the thought of a suffering-free eternity there, with God himself having wiped every tear from every eye, surely sets the sufferings of this present age in a somewhat different perspective. The New Testament gives tantalising hints of the resurrection body that awaits Christians on their deaths or on Christ's return, and therefore challenges us about the orientation our lives should have:

> . . . *many live as enemies of the cross of Christ. Their destiny is destruction, their god is their stomach, and their glory is in their shame. Their mind is on earthly things. But our citizenship is in heaven. And we eagerly await a Saviour from there, the Lord Jesus Christ, who, by the power that enables him to bring everything under his control, will transform our lowly bodies so that they will be like his glorious body.*
> (Philippians 3:18-21)

Elsewhere, Paul puts it, 'The first man was of the dust of the earth, the second man from heaven' (1 Corinthians 15:47). Christians believe there is always an eternal hope for healthcare. At least, they do in theory; whether they always do in practice is a challenge we will return to at the end of the book.

But supposing I don't believe the Bible?

This chapter has carefully considered a biblical view of what it means to be human. But Britain is probably more pluralistic and multicultural than ever. So why should we expect anybody else outside the church to take any notice of this sort of account? The answer is that many aspects of this sort of account square with the intuitions of patients and their families, and with those of fellow health professionals. Britain is probably more spiritual (if less religious) than ever before and mainstream medical literature is starting to reflect this. The Christian understanding of what it means to be human receives broad support from those of most other faiths, and often from those of no religious faith. This is so not least because of its consequences in the way we treat people.

As we will see in chapter six, *What has the church done historically?* there is a Christian tradition to healthcare in Britain that we take for granted without ever questioning where it comes from. It works very well – and it works because it's true rather than being true because it works.

No mean or ignoble animal?

Perhaps the last word should go to Thomas Sydenham (1624-1689), a famous Puritan physician who has a disease named after him but who is known as the English Hippocrates because of his concern for the methods of medicine and for its ethics. He reminds every practitioner of the privilege and purpose of medicine and of the status of all our patients:

Such skill and science as, by the blessing of Almighty God, he has allowed, are to be specially directed towards the good of his fellow-creatures: since it is a base thing for the great gifts of heaven to become the servants of avarice and ambition . . . He must remember that it is no mean or ignoble animal that he deals with . . . since for its sake God's only begotten Son became man, and thereby ennobled the nature he took upon Him.

References and Further Reading

Aitken JT, Fuller HW, Johnson D. *The Influence of Christians in Medicine.* London: Christian Medical Fellowship, 1984
ISBN 0 906747 11 2
Thomas Sydenham is referred to on pages 58, 128 & 173.

Grudem W. *Systematic Theology – an Introduction to Biblical Doctrine.* Leicester / Grand Rapids, Michigan: IVP / Zondervan, 1994
ISBN 0 85110 652 8
See chapter 23, *The Essential Nature of Man. What does Scripture mean by "soul" and "spirit"? Are they the same thing?*

Kidner D. *Genesis – an Introduction and Commentary.* London: Tyndale Press, 1967
ISBN 0 85111 823 2
The reference to Genesis 2:7 is on page 60.

3

What is health?

This must be a particularly hard question because nobody ever seems to ask it seriously! If we're going to spend £60 billion or more per annum (the approximate UK health budget in 2003) on something, surely we ought to know what it is we are spending our money on?

What do we want a definition of health for?

We need a definition of health for the hard practical reason just mentioned: we need to know what it is we are spending our money on; the reason we need to know that is so we can have some measure of it. As health service managers and others are so fond of saying, if we can't measure it we can't manage it.

Our definition will be shaped by our assumptions and values. Because healthcare is something we do for human beings, we need a definition that recognises what it means to be human. In the last chapter, we saw that humans are made in the image of God, are ensouled bodies and embodied souls, and are meant for relationships. It is in this area that the Christian worldview and its consequences come most sharply into conflict with the prevailing secular humanist worldview, which not only leaves out God but also omits almost all acknowledgement of the spiritual. This is the worldview that probably predominates still in British healthcare.

Our definition should not be so broad that it medicalises every part of life, taking responsibility away from where it belongs with each individual, nor one so narrow that it ignores the social and the spiritual. We need a definition that takes account of our responsibilities to each other in society, both in the small communities where we live and work, and in society at large, both nationally and internationally.

Finally, we need a definition that is theologically sound but also realistic, one which will work in the real world of the British National Health Service or in the desperate situation of an AIDS-stricken village in Africa.

Do we want a minimal biomedical definition?

In order to understand what health is, do we go for a minimal biomedical definition, such as the absence of disease or infirmity? (The source of this quote will become clear a little further on in the chapter.) Such a definition would be in line with the old joke: what is the doctor's definition of a healthy person? Somebody who hasn't been investigated adequately yet!

While such a definition may square with most people's first impression of what doctors, nurses and other health professionals do, it forces us to concentrate on the physical aspect of human nature, on man as a machine, on the body rather than the soul. It tends to turn doctors into mechanics of the human body who attempt to fix the broken parts. It is therefore concerned with cure (the relief of physical symptoms or the removal of pathology) rather than healing. This is a much broader concept, though it does not exclude cure; we will explore it further in chapter four. This minimal biomedical, purely physical approach has prevailed in British healthcare for a long time. It has been easy for critics to say that Britain has a National Sickness Service rather than a National Health Service.

I vividly remember sitting in the neurology clinic as a medical student, observing a consultation. A female patient came in. After a masterly history and examination, the Great Man diagnosed a psychiatric condition rather than an organic neurological disorder. At that time, psychiatry was not mentioned by name and the psychiatry department was second only to what was then called venereal diseases (now sexually transmitted infections) in having the most unattractive premises in the least accessible part of the hospital. The consultation ended: 'I have diagnosed that you have a chemical disorder of the brain and I am going to send you down the corridor to a colleague who specialises in chemical disorders of the brain'. 'Oh, thank you professor!' She beamed as she left. I wondered what her reaction would be when she discovered what her condition was thought to be and where it would be treated. Yet what really stuck with me were the professor's three words: 'Down the corridor'. I think I decided there and then I never wanted to be a down-the-corridor doctor. The memory of that consultation stayed with me and was doubtless involved in my eventual decision to go into general practice. Incidentally, while preparing to pass the membership examination for the Royal College of General Practitioners, I was expected to provide every patient I met with a physical diagnosis, a psychological diagnosis and a social diagnosis. I wanted to add the words 'a spiritual diagnosis'.

That consultation was thirty years ago. In the more recent past, the minimal biomedical approach has been seen most clearly in the healthcare of communist countries where the prevailing ideology was specifically atheist. If we are just bodies with no spiritual aspect, then healthcare professionals should devote themselves to caring for the body. Communism has given us vivid examples that what we believe controls what we do. Christianity should be giving us the same.

Minimal biomedical concepts have arisen from the reductionist approach. Philosophically, this examined the biblical concept of human beings as a whole of body and mind and spirit, and decided that if the spirit existed, the church could have responsibility for it. Body and mind were then separated, so to speak (as we saw in my neurology outpatients example); utilising all the new technology that was coming along, medical science focused in ever closer on the units and subunits of the body. As perhaps the ultimate illustration of this, society is now embarking on a debate about the safety and the ethics of nanotechnology, the use of atoms and molecules as machines for investigation and treatment. Scientific reductionism has of course been extremely helpful and led to many wonderful medical advances. These same advances have been accompanied by ever increasing expectations from our patients – they truly have come to expect a pill for every ill. The reductionist approach is fine as far as it goes. We just need to remember that it does not always go far enough.

Patients as individuals and western societies at large have reacted against this approach. Psychosomatic medicine started to repair the ravages of reductionism by putting mind and body back together. For example, we now accept that anxiety can cause people with asthma to wheeze more and that, conversely, wheezing can be frightening and can worsen anxiety. As we noted briefly in chapter two, a more holistic understanding of humanity is growing as a cultural phenomenon and has led many more people to acknowledge spiritual aspects of health.

Do we want a maximal all-inclusive definition?

At the other end of the spectrum are maximal all-inclusive definitions. The best known example is by the World Health Organisation (WHO):

> *The objective of WHO is the attainment by all peoples of the highest possible level of health. Health, as defined in the WHO Constitution, is a state of complete physical, mental and social well-being and not merely the absence of disease or infirmity.*

This definition goes much further towards being holistic. Although secular, it concurs partially with the biblical view of what it means to be human. Secular insights and intuition concur to this extent with biblical revelation. There is no mention of God or spirituality in this extract from the WHO's constitution, though they were acknowledging spiritual issues by 1998:

> *Until recently the health professions have largely followed a medical model, which seeks to treat patients by focusing on medicines and surgery, and gives less importance to beliefs and to faith – in healing, in the physician and in the doctor-patient relationship. This reductionist or mechanistic view of patients is no longer satisfactory. Patients and physicians have begun to realise the value of elements such as faith, hope, and compassion in the healing process. (WHO – see References and Further Reading at the end of the chapter.)*

From a Christian point of view, I support the sorts of concepts in the WHO definition but they fail at two extremes. On the one hand, they ignore the spiritual and in this respect do not contain enough. On the other hand, they contain too much and are impossibly utopian and unachievable. I don't think I have ever for one moment in my life enjoyed a state of complete social well-being. Surely I deserve an immediate NHS grant to help me achieve this? Obviously I am joking but that kind of thinking has crept into the expectations of patients who politically are now seen as consumers in a marketplace where the customer is always right. Unhelpfully, this leads politicians to unrealistic approaches to the delivery of healthcare. Perhaps some of our £60 billion could be spent more wisely?

This definition fails our requirement for realism. It will not work in the real worlds of the British National Health Service or an AIDS-stricken village in Africa.

We should remember that we Britons live as one of the most privileged groups of all time; yet the gap regarding health needs in our own nation is widening and globally the gap between rich and poor nations is widening even more. Maximal all-inclusive definitions can be almost offensive given the desperate health needs in so many parts of the world.

Is there a third way?

We need a definition of health that affirms our patients as whole people made in the image of God, who are both souls and bodies. We need a definition that works for the purposes of healthcare delivery in the real world, and which does not disenfranchise most of the planet's population.

When I was a GP I acquired, without ever seeking it, the privilege of working with many patients with profound physical and/or mental disabilities. They could not be cured. Anybody glancing at them would say immediately that they were obviously unhealthy. But in fact some of those people were more whole than me and I learned a great deal from them. Is there a definition of health that recognises that paradox? In 1989 radical restructuring was coming to the British National Health Service. In response a group of Christian health professionals and theologians met to consider what we then saw as the primary question: 'Good health – what is it?' The health professionals present were immediately attracted to a definition our theological colleagues shared with us.

Building on Karl Barth's definition, 'The power to be as man' (1961), the theologian Jürgen Moltmann described health as, 'The strength to be human' (1985). The first attraction about this is that healthcare can therefore be defined as giving more people more strength to be more human. This is a concept that would have helped me with my disabled patients. Indeed, it is a concept that would have helped me with all my patients. It helps any western health professional in any discipline. Such healthcare can always be achieved to some extent anywhere in the world. It does not disenfranchise any health professional or patient anywhere.

From a Christian point of view, it is a definition that does not contain any specifically biblical language, and that can be helpful in starting and maintaining a dialogue. But it does lead to specifically biblical ideas: thanks to human curiosity, the definition could never stand alone. It inevitably raises the obvious supplementary question: 'What do we mean by human?'

Of all the concepts referred to by the expression *in the image of God* (see chapter two), probably the most significant for the practice of healthcare is the idea of relationships. What does it mean to be human? It means having relationships.

Christians believe that each of us inevitably has relationships:

- with God
- with self
- with others
- with the environment

Those of other faiths and ideologies should broadly support the definition of health as the strength to be human, and it is a good basis for discussions in any country, culture or context. This definition of health influences the definitions of healing and healthcare and has profound implications for every aspect of practice. It has implications not just for health professionals but also for the whole of society and therefore the entire Christian church too.

Health: the strength to be human?

I have based the following discussion of the definition on the consensus statement on the nature of health produced in July 1989 by members of Caring Professions Concern, Christian Medical Fellowship, The Churches' Council for Health and Healing, Christian Impact, and Nurses' Christian Fellowship (see *References and Further Reading* at the end of the chapter).

Relationships

Christians define human-ness (and hence health) in terms of the following relationships. Ill-health arises from fractures and faults within them:

1) **With God** We saw in chapters one and two that we are made in the image of God and are intended to have a harmonious relationship with him. Sin, which is shorthand for the wrong choices we make and for the elevation of human judgment above divine command, destroys this relationship. The harmony is restored through repentance from sin, turning away from it and turning to personal faith in Christ's death on the cross, and then through acceptance of his lordship in our lives. This makes us spiritually whole. In chapter one we noted that this greater degree of wholeness was both natural through the deep and healing sense of forgiveness we experience, and supernatural through the indwelling of the Holy Spirit.

Psalm 32 shows powerfully how David understood his previously unconfessed sin as the cause of psychological distress and even physical disease. The cure came in finding forgiveness from God:

> *Blessed is he whose transgressions are forgiven, whose sins are covered. Blessed is the man whose sin the Lord does not count against him and in whose spirit is no deceit. When I kept silent, my bones wasted away through my groaning all day long. For day and night your hand was heavy upon me; my strength was sapped as in the heat of summer. Then I acknowledged my sin to you and did not cover up my iniquity. I said, "I will confess my transgressions to the Lord" – and you forgave the guilt of my sin. (Psalm 32:1-5)*

2) **With self** Physical disease can occur when different parts of the body fail to inter-relate properly. If the relationship between the thyroid gland and its target organs breaks down because the gland is not releasing enough thyroxine, then the many organs in question fail and the whole body slows down. The condition is readily reversible by supplying the missing hormone in tablet form.

Psychological disease includes failure to relate healthily to oneself. There is often a spiritual element in this, as the example of David in Psalm 32 shows. His deep-seated guilt made him unable to accept himself and caused depression.

3) **With others** Healthy relationships are needed between individuals. All GPs are familiar with the psychological and physical health consequences of broken marriages and failed sexual partnerships. Similarly, distress and even disease can occur after the breakdown of family relationships. On a larger scale, broken relationships within communities and societies, both nationally and internationally, can cause health problems consequent upon conflict or health inequalities consequent upon gross financial inequalities.

4) **With the environment** In chapter two we saw that we have a mandate to be stewards of the whole of creation. We are accountable to God for what we have done with it. With a few honourable exceptions, Christians generally got into the ecology debate much later than they should have done. We should respect God's creation for its own sake and for the benefit of our health. Now we are all familiar with the relationship between ecological concerns and health. For example, overuse of fossil fuels produces excess greenhouse gases; these deplete the ozone layer, causing increased radiation to reach us and cause skin cancer.

Healthism

We must beware the idolatry of healthism. Here the primary relationship with God is neglected and there can be an unhealthy obsession with our own state. Some of us come to worship our own bodies. Through advertising we are bombarded with images of health all the time. Health clubs and gyms abound and are two of many factors responsible for keeping people out of churches on Sundays. Without realising it, people often damage their physical health through the lengths they go to in order to become healthy, or at least to appear fit. Sun bed burns, steroid abuse, strains and sprains are just a few examples. Damage to psychological, social and spiritual health may be more subtle but even more serious in the long run.

There is a joke about two middle-aged executives who regularly go jogging together. At the top of a hill one of them has a cardiac arrest. Sadly, resuscitation is unsuccessful. The other executive's epitaph is revealing: 'What a way to go – in the peak of condition!'

Shalom

Health is linked with wholeness, and is part of the Biblical concept of *shalom*. Often translated peace, shalom means more than the absence of conflict; it involves wholeness, well-being, vigour and vitality in all the dimensions of human life. At that 1989 conference, one senior public health physician said that the government needed to introduce a Ministry of Shalom! It is a glorious ideal but we must accept that none of us will know shalom fully this side of heaven.

Health: the strength to be human is an all-embracing, ideal definition. We may legitimately need to use more specific functional definitions of health for particular tasks, yet must always beware taking too narrow a view of health.

Applications of the definition

This broad definition of health leads to the following applications:

• Public policy on health

This must mean more than the provision of medical services and must refer to all the relationships outlined above. For example, spiritual well-being, stable families, better housing, less hazardous workplaces and safer transport would all improve health. Whilst government and society would need to make sacrifices to achieve these and they would cost money in the short term, in the longer term they would be cost-effective. Increased taxation on alcohol and tobacco could generate money for healthcare; if higher taxes depressed consumption, this fiscal policy would also improve both individual and public health. The policy would give more people more strength to be more human.

• Resource allocation

Consideration of resource allocation is always controversial. There are three important principles that are related and need to be kept in balance.

1) **Justice** We should treat people rightly according to need. The Christian Medical Fellowship's Affirmation on Christian Ethics in Medical Practice states, for example in relation to patients, that we should '…give effective service to those seeking our medical care irrespective of age, race, creed, politics, social status or the circumstances which may have contributed to their illness'.

2) **Equity** We should provide equal access to healthcare, according to need, with financial factors being no deterrent. That is not to beg the enormous question of how healthcare should be funded. Healthcare free at the point of delivery has been a great strength of the British NHS, but I have lost count of the number of times I have heard people say healthcare in Britain is free. It is not: it is very expensive.

3) **Concern for the disadvantaged** We have a responsibility to take particular care of the defenceless. These include the unborn, babies, children, those with disabilities, asylum seekers, refugees, those with dementia, and the elderly. Sometimes such concern may require positive discrimination.

• Global view

We have a worldwide responsibility to all our fellow humans. The West should increase genuine aid to healthcare services in developing countries. It should also be wary of political initiatives such as sanctions, which intend to weaken rogue governments but actually harm the weakest people in such societies.

• Decision-making

Healthcare should always be provided as efficiently as possible, but to judge efficiency by financial measures alone is inappropriate, inadequate and immoral. Earlier, I mentioned with approval the importance of being able to measure in order to be able to manage. Yet, sometimes we have come to measure the unimportant, just because it can easily be assessed, whilst neglecting the important because it cannot easily be measured.

The whole community, not just healthcare professionals, should be involved in making judgments about resource allocation. This first became well known through an experiment in Oregon where all the citizens were consulted about how the State health budget should be spent. In 1995 our local health authority consulted community groups to see how they thought local budgets should be allocated. I was pleased that my own church hosted the meeting when researchers consulted Christians in the borough.

• Christian responsibility

The Christian church everywhere should be encouraged to recognise its responsibility to promote healthcare in the broadest sense, and to mobilise its undoubted resources. The example I have just given shows that churches are central in the community, and that Christians are generally better organised at the grassroots than other groupings within society.

Do the definition and its applications still work?

Fifteen years on, there have been a double figure number of reorganisations in the National Health Service. Although governments have put in much new money, staff morale is low and there is much dissatisfaction expressed by staff, patients and the media. It is not clear whether this dissatisfaction is justified and based on real and objective criteria, or whether it is a subjective one caused by unrealistic expectations.

But I found it interesting reviewing that consensus statement. It seems to be as valid today in the heightened complexities of the 21st century as it was back in the late 1980s. Survival over time is sometimes a reasonable test of the strength of an idea. Health is the strength to be human may remain the best definition of health to date.

References and Further Reading

Affirmation on Christian Ethics in Medical Practice.
Available from Christian Medical Fellowship, 157 Waterloo Road, London SE1 8XN

Culliford L. Spirituality and clinical care. *British Medical Journal* 2002; 325:1434-1435
Fergusson A (Ed). *Health: the strength to be human.* Leicester: CMF/IVP, 1993
ISBN 0 85110 981 0
See chapter one, *Towards a Theology of Health*, by David Atkinson for the analysis leading to his identification of Moltmann's definition. The consensus statement referred to can be found on pages 9-11.

World Health Organization. *WHOQOL and spirituality, religiousness and personal beliefs: report on WHO consultation.* Geneva: WHO, 1998

4

What is healing?

So far we have considered the Christian worldview; understood that being human means being a unity of body and soul made in the image of God and intended for relationships; and adopted a middle ground definition that health is the strength to be human. The next hard question is: 'What is healing?'

What different perspectives are there?

I chair the Acorn Christian Foundation, a large body that was founded in 1983, working in what I sometimes call 'the sensible end' of Christian healing. At a conference in 2002, I was on the platform with several of the senior staff, exploring how health professionals and the church might more effectively work together. There were about a hundred people present but only ten or so were health professionals; it was therefore a gathering mainly of lay Christians. I presented a fairly complex case history, modified from a real life one:

- Angie is 28 and is described as having 'social problems'.
- She has three children, the youngest three years old.
- She has had two terminations of pregnancy and two spontaneous miscarriages.
- After the birth of her youngest child, she had a sterilisation operation. It failed and she became pregnant again with an ectopic pregnancy.
- She underwent emergency surgery to remove the tube and the (dead) baby.
- You meet her on the ward the day after the surgery.

I asked the participants to work in pairs for a while, answering two questions:

- In what areas might healing be needed?
- How could such healing be provided?

They reported back after ten minutes of lively discussion. The answers were all around her immediate grief in bereavement, the need for social care for her three children, the need for inner healing because of inevitable guilt over the abortions, her relationship with the father or fathers of her eight pregnancies, her need to forgive the surgeon who had failed to sterilise her effectively, her need to find peace with God, and so on.

These were fascinating answers and not the ones most of the one million staff working in the National Health Service would have thought of first. The health professionals in the audience were strangely silent; over coffee afterwards, several agreed with me that I had been right in raising their sorts of questions:

- Is her post-operative pain adequately controlled?
- Is she on prophylactic antibiotics?
- Is she having treatment to prevent deep venous thrombosis?
- What is the state of her other uterine tube?
- Is she passing urine satisfactorily?
- Is she able to get to the toilet comfortably?

It is tempting to criticise the health professionals for being concerned solely with the physical aspects of Angie's needs, and conversely to criticise the lay Christians for being so heavenly minded as to be no earthly use. Yet the exercise demonstrated the very different perspectives the two constituencies have. In chapter eight we will look in more detail at ways the church and health professionals can work together more effectively to provide holistic healthcare.

How can we define healing?

Healing appears to mean different things to professionals and the laity. This is because they have different understandings of health, each having only a partial view. At its simplest, healing is movement towards health. Different understandings of healing will arise if there are different understandings of health. If the professionals are, perhaps quite properly, adopting a narrow functional definition of health in order to get on with their particular tasks of removing pathology or relieving physical symptoms, then their understanding of healing will be narrowed. This may not matter in any particular clinical context but professionals should discipline themselves to stand back periodically and take a broader view. The involvement of lay Christians could be very helpful here.

Therefore, a balanced consideration of healing demonstrates some of the applications of the definition of health we looked at in the last chapter: for example, that the whole community should be involved. Christianity recognises and endorses community and we should be supportive of initiatives in which communities are genuinely consulted. Still, we need to go deeper than the superficial focus group that panders to managers' expectations of consumers in the cultural context of the customer always being right.

What is healthcare?

If healing is defined as movement towards health, then healthcare is the process by which healing is helped to occur. One of my aims in this book is to try to bridge the artificial gap between the role of the health professional (be they Christian or not) in the technical aspects of healthcare, and the lay Christian who (inside or outside the church) is concerned about bringing healing, through prayer, symbols or acts of practical service. These approaches are both aiming at one common end – helping a patient on a journey towards healing and wholeness.

It is not therefore a question of one approach or the other. In the language of the old cliché, it is not a case of pills *or* prayer but a case of pills *and* prayer.

I dressed the wound – God healed him?

How close is the relationship between our healing endeavours, be they those of the health professional or the praying church, and any beneficial effect? Do we ourselves ever directly produce healing?

We would do well to remember at all times the saying of Ambroîse Paré (1510-1590), a Parisian barber-surgeon remembered for his integrity and sympathetic caring attitudes, but best known surgically for being the first to abandon the use of cautery in the treatment of gunshot wounds. Because his battlefield dressing station was overwhelmed by the numbers of wounded being brought in following the attack on the Château de Villare near Turin, Paré and his colleagues ran out of the boiling oil used for cauterising wounds, and therefore had to treat subsequent casualties with an application of cold egg yolk and rose oil in turpentine. The next morning, the second group (in what became an early example of a controlled trial) had passed a good night, with little or no pain, and their wounds showed no inflammation. There and then Paré abandoned the use of cautery for military wounds. Later, being congratulated for a similar success, he replied in Old French, *'Je le pensyt, Dieu le guaryt'* – 'I dressed it [the wound], God healed him'.

Whenever we are involved therapeutically in healthcare today, we are usually maximising the conditions so that the body's inbuilt healing mechanisms can take effect most rapidly. The boiling oil just added to tissue damage, while the second application soothed and reduced inflammation, allowing the body's healing processes to work more effectively. Even the most sophisticated surgery today depends similarly on the body's own processes, and it would be salutary for all health professionals to reflect on that from time to time.

It may be that prayer for healing most often works in this way too, maximising conditions so that the body's inbuilt healing mechanisms can take place most effectively. This may occur at a natural or supernatural level. We will consider this further in the chapter, *How can Christians pray for healing?*

What is the relationship between healing and salvation?

Salvation (to be saved) is a piece of jargon we have not used before. Being saved is the outcome of the process of redemption, the third theological pillar we consider. Of the four gospel writers, it is only Luke the physician who details the story of Zacchaeus:

> *'Jesus entered Jericho and was passing through. A man was there by the name of Zacchaeus; he was a chief tax collector and was wealthy. He wanted to see who Jesus was, but being a short man he could not, because of the crowd. So he ran ahead and climbed a sycamore-fig tree to see him, since Jesus was coming that way. When Jesus reached the spot, he looked up and said to him, "Zacchaeus, come down immediately. I must stay at your house today." So he came down at once and welcomed him gladly.*
>
> *All the people saw this and began to mutter, "He has gone to be the guest of a 'sinner'." But Zacchaeus stood up and said to the Lord, "Look, Lord! Here and now I give half of my possessions to the poor, and if I have cheated anybody out of anything, I will pay back four times the amount." Jesus said to him, "Today salvation has come to this house, because this man, too, is a son of Abraham. For the Son of Man came to seek and to save what was lost." (Luke 19:1-10)*

Here we see redemption in action. Jesus, describing himself with the enigmatic expression, 'the Son of Man', has come '…to seek and to save what was lost'. He initiates the relationship with Zacchaeus who clearly repents, as demonstrated in his new approach to his wealth, and who will clearly have healthier relationships from then on. Jesus says of this transformed man: 'Today salvation has come to this house'.

The Greek word *sozo* translated here as salvation could equally well be translated healing. Instead of saying Zacchaeus had been saved, or (using my word) transformed, we could say he had been healed. Salvation and healing are synonymous. Many Old Testament uses of the word healing make this clear. Health can only ever be complete in a saving relationship with Christ; this must be the ultimate goal for every Christian health professional. This is part of the concept of *shalom* (the wholeness, well-being, vigour and vitality in all the dimensions of human life) mentioned in chapter three.

What is the relationship between healing and wholeness?

This really follows from the link between healing and salvation. The words heal, whole, hale (as in 'hale and hearty'), and holy all share the same Anglo-Saxon root. Their concepts are linked and concern a common oneness. Somebody who is truly healed is whole and, given the link between healing and salvation, is holy. God said to the people of Israel in the Old Testament, 'I am the Lord your God; consecrate yourselves and be holy, because I am holy' (Leviticus 11:44). Peter reinforces this in the New Testament by quoting it to the expanding Christian church: 'But just as he who called you is holy, so be holy in all you do; for it is written: "Be holy, because I am holy"' (1 Peter 1:15-16).

What is the difference between healing and cure?

It may be helpful to differentiate healing, in this sense of *shalom* wholeness, from cure. Cure can be thought of as the relief of physical or psychological symptoms and/or the removal of physical pathology. Much of what modern medicine does is to bring cure only, and that may be fine as far as it goes. Healing includes but is more than cure.

In the last chapter, we looked at the question, 'What is health?' We noted that many in contemporary society elevate body above soul. They elevate the physical above the psychological, the social and the spiritual; they worship their own bodies in the idolatry of healthism. This behaviour is broadly parallel to being concerned only for cure at the expense of being concerned for healing.

In chapter seven we will consider some of the recent controversies in certain sections of the church about the outcome of prayer for healing. Among these misunderstandings we will see that, like secular society, some sections of the church are probably more concerned about curing than healing. The church is almost always more affected by surrounding culture than it affects that culture. It picks up the values of society, often without realising it.

Nine cured, one healed?

Again, Luke is the only one of the four Gospel writers to record a passage that shows the difference between cure and healing:

> *'Now on his way to Jerusalem, Jesus travelled along the border between Samaria and Galilee. As he was going into a village, ten men who had leprosy met him. They stood at a distance and called out in a loud voice, "Jesus, Master, have pity on us!" When he saw them, he said, "Go, show yourselves to the priests." And as they went, they were cleansed. One of them, when he saw he was healed, came back, praising God in a loud voice. He threw himself at Jesus' feet and thanked him – and he was a Samaritan. Jesus asked, "Were not all ten cleansed? Where are the other nine? Was no-one found to return and give praise to God except this foreigner?" Then he said to him, "Rise and go; your faith has made you well."' (Luke 17:11-19)*

Ten men were cured although the original Greek word applies to a range of disorders affecting the skin and does not necessarily signify the bacillary disease leprosy itself. Jesus miraculously removed their physical pathology, their signs and symptoms. They were cleansed. In obedience to his command, they went to show themselves to the priests who at that time had a role (of diagnosis and defining defilement) that bridged the roles of public health physician and priest.

Yet only one of the ten came back, '…praising God in a loud voice'. 'He threw himself at Jesus' feet and thanked him.' Leprosy, then as often now, did not just affect the sufferer physically. To prevent transmission of infection (and the Greek word translated leprosy could be applying to far more contagious conditions), the sufferer was separated from family and friends. He was unemployable. There were clear psychological and social effects of the skin stigmata. In view of the ritual defilement, there were spiritual consequences too. Therefore, the cure of the disease had the potential to bring further benefits. But nine of the ten only achieved the psychological and social benefits. They were probably off celebrating, making love with their wives, or looking for work, and I suspect I would have been among their number had I been in their position! Only one man (a Samaritan, and there is a separate point being made here) came back; only he fully realised the spiritual benefit; only he was healed. This example of 'nine cured, one healed' points us towards the greater goal of spiritual wholeness.

What is inner healing?

Inner healing is an expression that was heard more in the 1980s and early 1990s than it is now. Most people using it are referring to the healing of damaged emotions and painful memories. God's grace (meaning his unmerited giving) and forgiveness come in to the painful parts of the psyche, producing healing. The memories themselves do not disappear. Folklore tells us, 'Forgive and forget'; whilst I agree that we must forgive, in my experience people can rarely forget. What they can do is to come to terms with the memories associated with the incident, after they have forgiven, as necessary, the others involved. Our surgical wounds do not disappear as they heal up but we come to live comfortably with the scar tissue. Jesus rose from the dead in his resurrection body with the scars of crucifixion still in his hands, feet and side. Inner healing is about coming to live comfortably with the scar tissue in our souls.

I prefer not to use the expression inner healing: it seems to me that by an explicit *inner* healing there is an implicit *outer* healing. I am concerned about the concept of several levels of healing, preferring rather the distinction between curing and healing I make above. The concept of different levels seems to argue against the oneness that healing and wholeness are meant to be all about.

What is healing wounded history?

Although I prefer not to use the label *inner healing*, I readily acknowledge the effects of past hurts and their associated painful memories in relationships between individuals. They need healing. Perhaps more complex is the concept of such hurts and memories in the lives of communities of people. Russ Parker, Director of the Acorn Christian Foundation, has for some years been exploring the power of wounded group stories and the effects of these stories on the people and places where they first occurred. He argues that history tends to repeat itself unless we listen to and learn from history and, through strategic prayer, bring healing to families, churches, communities, tribes and nations.

This is a difficult area. Christian doctors were divided two decades ago over the concept of *healing the family tree*. My view is that we cannot change the past but we can change the effect the past has on the present. Again and again, we have seen that Christianity is about relationships and endorses community. No true concept of health can exist without wholeness in community.

All health professionals readily accept the importance of community. As a GP I had about 2,000 patients on my list. Each patient was an individual when they came into the consulting room and began to answer my question, 'What can I do for you?' At the same time, I was expected to consider all 2,000 as a community and target healthcare to that whole population. God cares about the health of whole communities as well as of individuals. There is a challenge to the Christian church to take on a role analogous to that of the public health physician and get involved appropriately in healing wounded history.

Is healing an event or a journey?

All health professionals recognise that healing is not an event but a journey. I was a great believer in prescribing 'tincture of time' to my patients. Many conditions are self-limiting and will cure themselves as the body's healing mechanisms do their work. Sometimes we need to intervene, prescribing medicines or surgery to maximise the conditions for these healing mechanisms to work. Sometimes we need to intervene very quickly indeed. Medical training is about learning the difference!

Bishop Morris Maddocks once described Christian healing as '...the difference made by Jesus when he meets us at our point of need'. When I first heard that, I thought it was hopelessly woolly, so heavenly minded as to be no earthly use. Some years on, after theoretical reflection and cautious pastoral practice in the area of Christian healing, I can see much more the wisdom of it.

In this chapter we saw Jesus meet Zacchaeus and heal him psychologically, socially and spiritually. We saw him meet ten lepers, cure nine and heal one. In the next chapter we will consider some further events when Jesus intervened dramatically in people's lives and met them at their point of need. In addition to events, we must also consider the healing effect of Jesus going with us on our journey through life. However, we can only know his presence by our side if we respond in faith to his invitation:

> *Come to me, all you who are weary and burdened, and I will give you rest. Take my yoke upon you and learn from me, for I am gentle and humble in heart, and you will find rest for your souls. For my yoke is easy and my burden is light. (Matthew 11:28-30)*

References and Further Reading

Aitken JT, Fuller HWC, Johnson D. *The Influence of Christians in Medicine*. London: Christian Medical Fellowship, 1984.
ISBN 0 906747 11 2
The incidents mentioned about Ambroîse Paré are featured on pages 53-55.

Wimber J with Springer K. *Power Healing*. London: Hodder and Stoughton, 1986.
ISBN 0 340 39090 5
There is a helpful discussion about inner healing on page 77.

Parker R. *Healing Wounded History: Reconciling peoples and healing places*. London: Darton, Longman and Todd, 2001.
ISBN 0 232 52251 0

5

What does the Bible say?

Christians believe God has revealed himself to us in writing in the Bible. This is therefore a key resource for finding out what God wants us to know. Church tradition can also be helpful sometimes, both in a positive sense and because we can learn from the Church's mistakes! God has also given us human reason and we should apply that to the full in everything we consider. Of these three resources – the Bible, Church tradition and reason – the Bible is the most reliable.

Although we have the Bible as a single volume, it is in fact a library of 66 books recording all we need to know of God's mind. The books fit into different sections of the library (Old and New Testaments with their various parts) and into different literary genres (history, law, poetry, wisdom literature, prophecy and letters). The individual books therefore need to be interpreted accordingly.

Having noted that we need to interpret it carefully, the Bible is nevertheless true and reliable. We should follow the line Paul takes as he commends his young protégé Timothy: '…how from infancy you have known the holy Scriptures, which are able to make you wise for salvation through faith in Christ Jesus. All Scripture is God-breathed and is useful for teaching, rebuking, correcting and training in righteousness, so that the man of God may be thoroughly equipped for every good work' (2 Timothy 3:15-17).

There are certain great themes within the Bible and to interpret it safely and reliably we need a scheme for considering them all, thus ensuring a balanced and comprehensive analysis. I use the four thematic pillars of:

Creation – how was it?

Fall – how is it?

Redemption – how could it be/how should it be?

Future hope – how will it be?

We particularly studied the pillar of Creation in chapter two, *What does it mean to be human?* and we will examine the Fall further in chapter 13, *Why does God allow suffering?* In chapter three, we briefly considered the biblical underpinning for health as 'the strength to be human'. In this chapter I will mainly be considering health and healing under the concept of *Redemption – how could it be/how should it be?* I will end the book with some reflections on *Future hope – how will it be?*

The Bible's frequent link between healing and salvation, what we might call the spiritual aspect of healing, has been considered in chapter four, *What is healing?* The Bible discusses what we might call medical healing, healing of body and mind, mainly but not entirely in supernatural terms of miraculous intervention. We will now look at these medical aspects as they are discussed in the different sections of the biblical library.

What is in the Old Testament?

This first part of the Bible deals with God's relationship with people before the time of Christ.

What does the Old Testament say about medical aspects of health?

The basic moral code given to God's people in the Ten Commandments (Exodus 20:1-17 and Deuteronomy 5:6-21) is amplified in parts of Leviticus and Deuteronomy that are commonly called the Levitical Code. The moral code is applied to the details of daily life and much consideration is given to what defiles a man or woman and therefore makes him or her unclean. In *The Levitical Code: Hygiene or Holiness*, public health doctor Averell Darling poses this question: 'Was the code designed purely for ceremonial purposes, or was it a programme of health and hygiene? Or could it possibly have been intended as a combination of the two?'

He goes on to point out the practical advantages to the Israelites. The sexual and marriage requirements of the code would maintain health in terms of freedom from sexually transmitted infections and from some genetic disorders. He notes the public health benefits for the Hebrew encampment in the regulations about sewage disposal, burial of the dead, quarantine regulations for some infectious diseases, as well as food, clean water, air, clothing and dwellings. Israel was in these respects well ahead of neighbouring nations at the time.

He notes that our word quarantine is derived from this Old Testament Code. During the fourteenth century there were epidemics of severe plague in Italy. The Jews were afflicted less often and it was suspected this might be connected with their ceremonial washings and rules concerning touching bodies and early burial. The regulations of Leviticus 12:1-4 became adopted into public law, and the Italian quaranta (forty) came to describe the prescribed number of days for isolating patients and infectious contacts.

Darling goes on to consider the ceremonial aspects of defilement under five alliterative headings: diet, delivery, discharges, death, and dermatitis! He finds the public health benefits, although considerable, limited and concludes: 'It does seem, therefore, that though the primary purpose of the code was to help in the separation of a holy nation unto a holy God, it also had its incidental value in the development of some forms of hygiene that are of benefit today'.

Perhaps in his scholarly critique Darling has seen as too limited the extent of the medical benefits. As the aftermath of war and disaster fills our television screens almost daily, we are forcibly reminded that health priorities include clean food, water, air, clothing, and housing. They include disposing of sewage, burying the dead, and the control of infectious disease.

Whatever we conclude on Darling's question about hygiene or holiness, the fact that the Levitical Code was given several thousand years before any factual knowledge of the issues had been gained from human sources convinces me that it must have been 'God-breathed'. Parts of it significantly help health professionals to 'be thoroughly equipped for every good work'.

What does the Old Testament say about miracles of healing?

Collins English Dictionary (21st Century Edition, 2000) defines a miracle as: '1 an event contrary to the laws of nature and attributed to a supernatural cause. 2 any amazing or wonderful event. 3 a marvellous example of something: *a miracle of engineering*'. Part of the controversy about healing that we will consider later, particularly in chapter seven, is that participants in the miraculous healing debate are often using not the first but the second or third definitions listed. I argue strongly that we should reserve the word miracle for the first definition only – 'an event contrary to the laws of nature and attributed to a supernatural cause' – and that is the only sense in which I now use it.

Miracles in the Old Testament are comparatively rare occurrences and are mainly confined to times of deliverance: the Exodus of Israel from captivity in Egypt and the prophetic ministry of Elijah and Elisha during another spell of captivity under the oppression of Ahab and Jezebel.

Miracles of healing are even more infrequent, most being miracles of:

- **nature** – Aaron's staff budding (Numbers 17), an iron axe-head floating (2 Kings 6)
- **provision** – manna and quail as food (Exodus 16), oil for the widow (2 Kings 4)
- **revelation of God's will** – Balaam's donkey speaking (Numbers 22), Gideon's crossover trial with a fleece (Judges 6)
- **preservation** – from the fiery furnace (Daniel 3), from inside the fish (Jonah 1-2)
- **judgment** – ten plagues on Egypt (Exodus 7-11), fire from heaven (2 Kings 1)

Miracles of judgment are the most numerous! There are only eight healing miracles in the Old Testament, including three cases of raising the dead (see Appendix 1). Although occasionally natural means are involved, each of these events is clearly supernatural. I choose one of the eight at random to illustrate that it has all the characteristics of New Testament miracles.

> *Then the Lord said, "Put your hand inside your cloak." So Moses put his hand into his cloak, and when he took it out, it was leprous, like snow. "Now put it back into your cloak," he said. So Moses put his hand back into his cloak, and when he took it out, it was restored, like the rest of his flesh. (Exodus 4:6-7)*

This example is slightly unusual in that, while demonstrating to a reluctant Moses the power he will later show Pharaoh, God creates a case of disease and cures it immediately. We saw in chapter four that, in the Bible, the word leprosy is used for various diseases affecting the skin and not necessarily the one specific bacillary disease. Nevertheless, this example demonstrates all the following:

- The condition was an obvious example of gross physical disease
- It was at that time incurable (and no instant cure would be possible today)
- No physical means were used
- The cure was immediate
- Restoration was complete and therefore obvious
- There was no recorded relapse
- The miracle helped Moses' faith (somewhat!)

This miracle, and any of the other seven healing miracles in the Old Testament, clearly fits the first dictionary definition as, 'An event contrary to the laws of nature and attributed to a supernatural cause'. So do all the New Testament miracles we turn to now.

What is in the New Testament?

The second part of the Bible deals with the life and ministry of Jesus Christ and with the activities of the early Christian church. The Appendices at the end of this book list Jesus' healing miracles of individuals, groups and crowds, and healings performed through the apostles and other disciples as recorded in the gospels and Acts. Take a few minutes now to read the very brief descriptions there and see the range of conditions covered. Later on, study all the original Bible passages.

By contrast with the Old Testament, healings now appear on almost every page of the gospels. One fifth of the gospels is taken up with accounts of Jesus' healings and what followed. There are in total 25 individual healings and 16 descriptions of large group healings. However, we should note at the outset that although there is no record of Jesus ever rejecting anybody who asked for healing, he did not always heal everyone in need. In John 5:1-15 at the pool of Bethesda, '...a great number of disabled people used to lie – the blind, the lame, the paralysed' but he only healed '...one who . . . had been an invalid for thirty-eight years'.

The Appendices list references to the *what, when* and *where* of the healings, and we consider examples throughout this book. We also need to look carefully at the questions of *how* and *why*.

How did Jesus heal?

Dr Peter May has analysed the characteristics of Christ's miracles of healing and of the others seen in the Bible.

- **The conditions were obvious examples of gross physical disease**
  As we look at the range of conditions in the Appendices – paralysis, deafness, blindness, death – there would have been no doubt whatsoever to observers that something major was wrong! (The particular question of the descriptions of people as possessed by evil spirits, and any possible relationship with psychiatric or physical disease, will be considered further in chapter nine, *Do demons cause disease and death?*)

- **They were at that time incurable and most remain so today**
  Modern medical science can of course help deafness and eye conditions short of total blindness. It can even help total blindness in some circumstances, and there are reports emerging of electrodes being implanted to help cases of paralysis, but the cures of Jesus were not explicable naturally. They met the first dictionary definition of miracles.

- **Jesus almost never used physical means**
  He spoke sometimes, he touched often, and presumably he prayed, but he did not use medication or surgery. John 9:6 is one possible exception: 'He spat on the ground, made some mud with the saliva, and put it on the man's eyes'. The reason for this is obscure.

- **The cures were immediate**
  These were not gradual improvements over hours, days or weeks, and therefore perhaps difficult to discriminate from natural recoveries, whether these natural recoveries were in any way accelerated or otherwise. These cures happened immediately and were clearly events contrary to the laws of nature. There is one possible exception in a two stage healing of blindness described in Mark 8:22-26 where again the reason is obscure.

- **Restoration was complete and therefore obvious**
  In Matthew 12 Jesus engages in controversy with the Pharisees about healing on the Sabbath (a day of rest prescribed by God which the ruling religious party had misunderstood and were legalistic about). The healing concerns a man with a shrivelled hand. After a time of teaching about the value of human beings and the purpose of the Sabbath, we read of Jesus: 'Then he said to the man, "Stretch out your hand." So he stretched it out and it was completely restored, just as sound as the other' (Matthew 12:9-13). In this example there is no doubt whatsoever there had been a total cure.

- **There were no recorded relapses**
  It is consistent neither with biblical truthfulness nor with logic that the conditions apparently cured could have recurred shortly afterwards without the record being revised. Some of the gospel accounts were circulating within the lifetime of those who had witnessed these miracles, and any such fraud would have been challenged successfully.

• **Miracles regularly elicited faith**
This might be faith on the part of the one cured, or faith in those around. We will consider the place of faith prior to Jesus' healings, whether that be faith of the patient or of others, in chapter eleven, *Must you have faith to be healed?*

These seven characteristics set a New Testament gold standard for defining healing miracles. In chapter seven, *What are Christians doing today?* we will assess whether contemporary claims for healing meet this gold standard and therefore deserve the first dictionary definition of a miracle.

Why did Jesus heal?

Dr Trevor Stammers has analysed the significance and purpose of the miracles along the following lines:

• **Because he was the Messiah**
Messiah (Hebrew) or *Christ* (Greek) means anointed one and Old Testament prophecies foretold that the Messiah would come. Two gospel passages relate the messianic expectation of healing to the person of Jesus:

> *...he drove out the spirits with a word and healed all the sick. This was to fulfil what was spoken through the prophet Isaiah: "He took up our infirmities and carried our diseases." (Matthew 8:16-17 where the reference is to Isaiah 53:4)*

> *He went to Nazareth, where he had been brought up, and on the Sabbath day he went into the synagogue, as was his custom. And he stood up to read. The scroll of the prophet Isaiah was handed to him. Unrolling it, he found the place where it is written: "The Spirit of the Lord is on me, because he has anointed me to preach good news to the poor. He has sent me to proclaim freedom for the prisoners and recovery of sight for the blind, to release the oppressed, to proclaim the year of the Lord's favour." Then he rolled up the scroll, gave it back to the attendant and sat down. The eyes of everyone in the synagogue were fastened on him, and he began by saying to them, "Today this scripture is fulfilled in your hearing." (Luke 4:16-21 where the reference is to Isaiah 61:1-2)*

• **Because he reveals the heart of God**
Jesus is the perfect expression of God's heart and there is therefore surely a sense in which he could not but heal. Jesus

said, 'I tell you the truth, the Son can do nothing by himself; he can do only what he sees his Father doing, because whatever the Father does the Son also does' (John 5:19). The miracles reveal something essential about the character of the Father.

- **Because he is compassionate**

The following examples make it clear that Jesus' healings are linked with the compassion that is central to God's character:

> *When Jesus landed and saw a large crowd, he had compassion on them and healed their sick. (Matthew 14:14)*

> *A man with leprosy came to him and begged him on his knees, "If you are willing, you can make me clean." Filled with compassion, Jesus reached out his hand and touched the man. "I am willing," he said. "Be clean!" Immediately the leprosy left him and he was cured. (Mark 1:40-42)*

> *As he approached the town gate, a dead person was being carried out – the only son of his mother, and she was a widow. And a large crowd from the town was with her. When the Lord saw her, his heart went out to her and he said, "Don't cry." Then he went up and touched the coffin, and those carrying it stood still. He said, "Young man, I say to you, get up!" The dead man sat up and began to talk, and Jesus gave him back to his mother. (Luke 7:12-15)*

In two extracts we read specifically of compassion and in the last we read, '…his heart went out to her', an expression beloved by today's media to typify the intuitive human response to grief.

- **Because his miracles are signs pointing to himself**

This is evident in Jesus' replies to John the Baptist and to his own disciples:

> *When John heard in prison what Christ was doing, he sent his disciples to ask him, "Are you the one who was to come, or should we expect someone else?" Jesus replied, "Go back and report to John what you hear and see: The blind receive sight, the lame walk, those who have leprosy are cured, the deaf hear, the dead are raised, and the good news is preached to the poor…" (Matthew 11:2-5)*

> *Believe me when I say that I am in the Father and the Father is in me; or at least believe on the evidence of the miracles themselves. (John 14:11)*

John's gospel is actually built around a number of miracles pointing as signs to Jesus' divinity:

> *'Jesus did many other miraculous signs in the presence of his disciples, which are not recorded in this book. But these are written that you may believe that Jesus is the Christ, the Son of God, and that by believing you may have life in his name'. (John 20:30-31)*

However, the significance of Christ's miracles needs to be held within a broader perspective. Jesus himself taught that miracles in themselves may not be a sign of much value:

> *'Many will say to me on that day, "Lord, Lord, did we not prophesy in your name, and in your name drive out demons and perform many miracles?" Then I will tell them plainly, "I never knew you. Away from me, you evildoers!"' (Matthew 8:22-23)*

- **Because he was inaugurating his kingdom**
  The kingdom of God exists when God's will holds perfect sway. The theologian Hans Küng has linked healing with the kingdom: *'...the kingdom of God is creation healed'*. The close link between Christ's healings and the kingdom is particularly prominent in Matthew's Gospel. He twice records that Jesus went about, *'...preaching the good news of the kingdom, and healing every disease and sickness'* (Matthew 4:23 and 9:35). Again, in Matthew 12:28 there is a clear association between miracles and the coming kingdom: *'But if I drive out demons by the Spirit of God, then the kingdom of God has come upon you'*.

What is for now and what is not yet?

This discussion of the kingdom takes us to a central paradox, to one of the hardest of all questions. It is the question about the tension between health and healing and their co-existence with suffering. We simply have to accept that some things are for now, and some things will always on this earth be not yet. I quote at length from theologian and pastor Peter Lewis in *Hope, Healing and the Charismatic Movement*:

> *The kingdom of God came in and with and by Jesus Christ, his only Son. At his coming, a new order entered our world in its disorder; first to rescue us in our old world and then to prepare us for God's new world. At first the kingdom of God came secretly with the birth of Jesus at Bethlehem. In time, it was openly announced and demonstrated in his ministry with words, works and wonders . . .*

The arrival of the kingdom of God, however, was always partial and provisional. It is already here, but not yet here in its fullness. It was, and is, and is yet to come . . .

. . . we are touched with both the glory of the world to come and the corruption of the world that is. We are justified children of God and sinful creatures; we are kept under the shadow of his wings and led into times of suffering like others; we have eternal life and dying bodies; we are healed and we sicken again. This is our glorious hope which does not disappoint us, and these are the grim realities it lives alongside . . .

That is why, even in the New Testament, miracles are never ordinary. What is ordinary is reliable conformity to wise and good natural laws. Nevertheless, in a disturbed creation, God in grace does interrupt his usual way of working, his natural order, for a greater good. He is not the prisoner of his own laws. But his kingdom-related activity is always extraordinary in the world as we know it. It is the partial and periodic invasion of one order by another. Miracles as the suspension or contradiction of natural laws are extraordinary signs of the kingdom which is coming; they are powers of an age to come breaking through.

The chief purpose of healing miracles is declaratory and revelatory rather than therapeutic. Even as healings, they are not so much a local response as a public statement, a promise that God in Christ will one day break the stranglehold of sin, sickness and death. The statement made in isolated instances points to the certainty that one day God will renew the face of the whole earth.

Peter Lewis' passion thrills us as we realise what we have *now* even in the face of suffering. His passion should thrill us even more about the *not yet*, although in the last chapter of the book we will consider whether Christians really believe deep down in their hearts in the reality of heaven. But this uncomfortable tension between the *now* and the *not yet* challenges Christians at both ends of the spectrum. Those who always want God's *not yet* now will regularly face disappointment and their initially high level of faith will be reduced. Those who can only see what could be God's *now* as always being *not yet* need their initially low level of faith increased.

The obvious question of course is: 'How do we know whether healing is *now* or *not yet?*' My short answer is a pastorally cautious,

'Let us pray and see what happens'. We will consider this in much greater detail in chapter twelve, *How should Christians pray for healing?*

Is there healing in the atonement?

We have already considered the cross-referencing between Isaiah's messianic prophecy and Christ's healings (Matthew 8:16-17). Some have appropriated this link to claim healing in the atonement: that, because of the fact of the cross, there is automatic and guaranteed healing from every disease for every Christian on every occasion. It should be clear by now that the biblical position is that no healings are automatic or guaranteed, but the cross, the atonement (which we can helpfully think of as the at-one-ment) is certainly about our wholeness and our *shalom* (see chapters three and four). While this is not primarily about cure in any physical sense it does not exclude it. So is there healing in the atonement? Yes – and no!

Does the Great Commission mean we should pray for healing today?

In chapter seven, *What are Christians doing today?* we will briefly consider the controversy in some sections of the church over Christian healing. A key question in that debate is: 'How much of the Bible's teaching about healing applies to us today?'

At the end of Matthew's Gospel, the ascension of Jesus into heaven after he has completed all his earthly work is preceded by what has been called the Great Commission:

> Then Jesus came to them and said, "All authority in heaven
> and on earth has been given to me. Therefore go and make
> disciples of all nations, baptising them in the name of the
> Father and of the Son and of the Holy Spirit, and teaching
> them to obey everything I have commanded you. And surely
> I will be with you always, to the very end of the age."
> (Matthew 28:18-20)

Does '…teaching them to obey everything I have commanded you' include the earlier commands to heal given in the commissioning, first of the twelve disciples and then of seventy-two?

> He called his twelve disciples to him and gave them authority
> to drive out evil spirits and to heal every disease and
> sickness…"As you go, preach this message: 'The kingdom of
> heaven is near.' Heal the sick, raise the dead, cleanse those who
> have leprosy, drive out demons." (Matthew 10:1, 7-8)

> *Calling the Twelve to him, he sent them out two by two and*
> *gave them authority over evil spirits...They went out and*
> *preached that people should repent. They drove out many*
> *demons and anointed many sick people with oil and healed*
> *them. (Mark 6:7, 12-13)*

> *When Jesus had called the Twelve together, he gave them power*
> *and authority to drive out all demons and to cure diseases, and*
> *he sent them out to preach the kingdom of God and to heal the*
> *sick...So they set out and went from village to village, preaching*
> *the gospel and healing people everywhere. (Luke 9:1-2, 6)*

> *After this the Lord appointed seventy-two others and sent them*
> *two by two ahead of him to every town and place where he was*
> *about to go. He told them, "...Heal the sick who are there and*
> *tell them 'The kingdom of God is near you'." (Luke 10:1-2, 9)*

There is some controversy about whether there is a similar commissioning at the end of Mark's gospel or not. The two most reliable early manuscripts end at Mark 16:8; nevertheless, most editions of the Bible add separately the longer ending of Mark 16:9-20. In his substantial commentary Donald English says: 'None of the proposed solutions to the problem of the ending of Mark is without objections or difficulties. Whether Mark meant to finish with verse 8, or his original ending got lost, verses 9-20 cannot with any confidence be accepted as an authentic part of his gospel. On the one hand, the scribe who added this conclusion did well by taking up Mark's theme of belief and unbelief, as we shall see, but on the other hand he credited Jesus with making promises of spectacular signs which do not harmonize with the main body of Mark's gospel'.

The IVP New Bible Commentary says, 'These verses...are not part of Scripture, and so we should not use them for establishing any doctrine, but they are still a valuable summary of the beliefs of the early church, and in so far as they agree with Scripture we may accept them'. On that basis, namely the extent to which they agree with Scripture, let us look at verses 15-18 which contain a somewhat similar but more detailed commissioning:

> *He said to them, "Go into all the world and preach the good*
> *news to all creation. Whoever believes and is baptised will be*
> *saved, but whoever does not believe will be condemned. And*
> *these signs will accompany those who believe: In my name*
> *they will drive out demons; they will speak in new tongues;*
> *they will pick up snakes with their hands; and when they drink*
> *deadly poison, it will not hurt them at all; they will place their*
> *hands on sick people, and they will get well."*

Preaching and baptising are not controversial and we have seen plenty elsewhere about driving out demons and healing the sick. New tongues are mentioned among the lists of spiritual gifts in 1 Corinthians; it is the snakes and the poison we should not be building a doctrine on! But for what it is worth, the end of Mark's gospel suggests a normative role for the laying on of hands (and presumably prayer) for healing.

This alternative ending to Mark's gospel concludes, 'Then the disciples went out and preached everywhere, and the Lord worked with them and confirmed his word by the signs that accompanied it'.

What happens in Acts?

The Acts of the Apostles follows the four gospels and describes how the early church grew rapidly, exactly as Christ had prophesied:

> '"But you will receive power when the Holy Spirit comes on you; and you will be my witnesses in Jerusalem, and in all Judea and Samaria, and to the ends of the earth"'. (Acts 1:8)

Appendix four lists healings performed by Jesus' followers as recorded in Acts. These healings have the same characteristics as Christ's and are clearly category one miracles. Sometimes they appear to go beyond Christ's.

> The apostles performed many miraculous signs and wonders among the people... people brought the sick into the streets and laid them on beds and mats so that at least Peter's shadow might fall on some of them as he passed by. Crowds gathered also from the towns around Jerusalem, bringing their sick and those tormented by evil spirits, and all of them were healed. (Acts 5:12-16)

> God did extraordinary miracles through Paul. Handkerchiefs and aprons that had touched him were taken to the sick, and their illnesses were cured and the evil spirits left them. (Acts 19:11-12)

Some Christians would see these as healing examples of what Jesus, having just spoken about 'the evidence of the miracles themselves', had promised his disciples on the last night: 'I tell you the truth, anyone who has faith in me will do what I have been doing. He will do even greater things than these, because I am going to the Father' (John 14:12). There have been intense debates about the 'greater things' – do they include healing or not? And do the promises made face-to-face to the disciples then apply to Christian disciples today? The IVP New Bible Commentary concludes: 'The statement of Jesus in v12 is surprising.

The believer would do *greater things than these.* Jesus had made clear that the believer would continue what he had been doing. But greater than that can be understood only in the light of the post-resurrection period during which the gospel would be proclaimed. It is clear that the greater things can be done only because Jesus is going to the Father. The book of Acts is evidence of the fulfilment of this prediction, and the worldwide spread of Christianity today a further sign of these 'greater things'. The close link between the promise and the attitude of prayer needed for its fulfilment is seen in vs 13-14'.

So, healing miracles continue in the Book of Acts. Sometimes they are linked with the effective proclamation of the Christian message, but there are also many examples of effective evangelism without any healing miracles. We should note also that there is no record in Acts of the church being taught to pray for healing.

What do the New Testament letters say?
Paul, an unknown writer to the Hebrews, James, Peter, John and Jude wrote the letters and generally they say a great deal less about healing than the gospels and Acts. Some have argued that because the apostolic era was over and the church had spread, the extraordinary outpouring of God's Spirit had ceased and there were no more miracles of healing. Hence there is little mention of healing. Others have argued that the letters were written to advise on controversies and healing was so widely established as a normal part of church life that there was no need to make much mention of it. So, what do the New Testament letters have to say?

What are gifts of healing?
Paul discusses spiritual gifts in Romans 12 and 1 Corinthians 12-14. He argues that each Christian has at least one spiritual gift and that it is there for blessing others.

> *Now to each one the manifestation of the Spirit is given for the common good. To one there is given through the Spirit the message of wisdom, to another the message of knowledge by means of the same Spirit, to another faith by the same Spirit, to another gifts of healing by that one Spirit, to another miraculous powers, to another prophecy, to another the ability to distinguish between spirits, to another the ability to speak in different kinds of tongues, and to still another the interpretation of tongues. All these are the work of one and the same Spirit, and he gives them to each one, just as he determines. (1 Corinthians 12:7-11)*

Spiritual gifts include both qualities and abilities we are born with and which we develop (nature developed by nurture), and supernatural powers. The gifts of healing do not exclude natural abilities – I hope I had at least some abilities relevant to being a doctor even before I went to medical school – but in this context probably refer to supernatural gifting. In chapter twelve, *How should Christians pray for healing?* I will argue that any such supernatural gifting has only a small part to play in Christian prayer for healing.

At the end of the chapter Paul stresses our mutual responsibilities and the corporate nature of Christian life, and puts gifts in their context:

> *Now you are the body of Christ, and each one of you is a part of it. And in the church God has appointed first of all apostles, second prophets, third teachers, then workers of miracles, also those having gifts of healing, those able to help others, those with gifts of administration, and those speaking in different kinds of tongues. Are all apostles? Are all prophets? Are all teachers? Do all work miracles? Do all have gifts of healing? Do all speak in tongues? Do all interpret? But eagerly desire the greater gifts. And now I will show you the most excellent way. (1 Corinthians 12:27-31)*

And what is the most excellent way? The next chapter of 1 Corinthians is a famous passage about love!

Did healing always happen?

I referred earlier to the two main interpretations of the relative silence about healing in the New Testament letters. Perhaps against those who argue that completely effective prayer for healing was so commonplace in the early church it did not need mentioning, we read of four cases where we know or can presume that prayer took place and where healing did not occur immediately if at all.

- **Epaphroditus**…*is distressed because you heard he was ill. Indeed he was ill, and almost died. But God had mercy on him, and not on him only but also on me...he almost died for the work of Christ, risking his life to make up for the help you could not give me. (Philippians 2:25-30)*
- **Timothy** *Stop drinking only water, and use a little wine because of your stomach and your frequent illnesses. (1 Timothy 5:23)*
- **Trophimus**...*and I left Trophimus sick in Miletus. (2 Timothy 4:20)*
- **Paul** *As you know, it was because of an illness that I first preached the gospel to you. Even though my illness was a trial to you, you did not treat me with contempt or scorn. Instead, you welcomed me as if I were an angel of God, as if I were Christ Jesus himself. (Galatians 4:13-14)*

There is another passage by Paul about himself which some have interpreted to refer to a failure of prayer for healing:

> *To keep me from becoming conceited because of these surpassingly great revelations, there was given me a thorn in my flesh, a messenger of Satan, to torment me. Three times I pleaded with the Lord to take it away from me. But he said to me, "My grace is sufficient for you, for my power is made perfect in weakness." Therefore I will boast all the more gladly about my weaknesses, so that Christ's power may rest on me.* (2 Corinthians 12:7-9)

Speculation about this thorn in the flesh has included it being a difficult personal relationship, persecution, sexual temptation or a painful physical ailment. An eye condition has been suggested because of Paul's statement in Galatians 6:11: 'See what large letters I use as I write to you with my own hand!' We cannot know for certain. This lack of specificity, which must have been deliberate and not an oversight, allows us to apply this passage legitimately to more situations than would otherwise be the case. I will return to it in chapter 13 on suffering.

Is there practical advice about prayer for healing?
Perhaps the most practical passage in the New Testament letters is in the book of James:

> *Is any one of you in trouble? He should pray. Is anyone happy? Let him sing songs of praise. Is any one of you sick? He should call the elders of the church to pray over him and anoint him with oil in the name of the Lord. And the prayer offered in faith will make the sick person well; the Lord will raise him up. If he has sinned, he will be forgiven. Therefore confess your sins to each other and pray for each other so that you may be healed. The prayer of a righteous man is powerful and effective.* (James 5:13-16)

The context of this passage is prayer and faith. James goes on to illustrate that '…the prayer of a righteous man is powerful and effective' by referring to Elijah, whose miracle ministry is considered briefly in this chapter and referred to in Appendix one. I believe the passage is relevant to the church today and we will consider it further line by line in chapter twelve, *How should Christians pray for healing?*

Jesus: infectious with wholeness?

We have considered the facts of Jesus' healings, and the how and the why. We have thought about the tension between the now and the not yet and the question of whether the healing is in the atonement. We have considered the rest of the New Testament more briefly, but let us end by remembering just how radical Christ was.

> *During the earthly ministry of Jesus, when he met people he was never a non-event. Those who met him in the first century AD were different afterward. He was "infectious" with wholeness...He made a difference to people physically, but the difference was much deeper than that. Not only did the lame walk, the deaf hear and the blind see, but new peace and sanity came to those who were mentally and emotionally tormented, and tarnished evildoers became clean and new. Lifestyles were transformed. Aims and attitudes were changed. There was a new relationship with people and with God...That was Christian healing, first-century style. It is still the essence of the Christian healing ministry.* (Roy Lawrence, *The Practice of Christian Healing – A Guide for Beginners*)

References and Further Reading

Carson DA, France RT, Motyer JA, Wenham GJ (Eds). *New Bible Commentary – 21st Century Edition*. Leicester: IVP, 1994
ISBN 0 85110 648 X
The discussion of the ending of Mark is on page 977. John 14:12 is discussed on page 1055.

Darling AS. *The Levitical Code: Hygiene or Holiness* in *Medicine and the Bible*. Exeter: CMF/Paternoster Press, 1986. ISBN 0 85364 423 3

English D. *The Message of Mark*. Leicester: IVP The Bible Speaks Today, 1992
ISBN 0 85110 968 3
The discussion of the ending of Mark is on page 240.

Lawrence R. *The Practice of Christian Healing – A Guide for Beginners*. Downer's Grove, Illinois: IVP Saltshaker, 1996
ISBN 0 8308 1960 6
The passage about Jesus being infectious with wholeness is on page 21.

Lewis P. *Hope, Healing and the Charismatic Movement* in *Christian Choices in Healthcare*. Leicester: CMF/IVP, 1995
ISBN 0 85111 144 0

Wilkinson J. *The Bible and Healing – a Medical and Theological Commentary*. Edinburgh/Grand Rapids, Michigan: Handsel Press Ltd/Wm. B Eerdmans, 1998
ISBN 1 871828 39 2/0 8028 3826 X

6

What has the church done historically?

The Christian church came into being shortly after the death and resurrection of Jesus, and in the last chapter we briefly considered healing aspects in its early life as recorded in the Book of Acts. The Bible was completed in the first century AD, and historical material thereafter is relatively sparse until much more recently. In this chapter we will take a brief look at the involvement of the Christian church and of individual Christians in matters of health and healing, up until the present time.

This would be a very different sort of book if there were to be a long list of names and dates and places. Such works do exist – see *References and Further Reading* at the end of this chapter. I will try to give a brief overview of two millennia, choosing a few medical areas only. This is not to imply that other areas are less important. I will reflect a little on my own years in general practice as I try to illustrate the principle that many innovative works (I was not the innovator) arose as Christians responded to needs, often in geographical areas or areas of medical practice that were not glamorous or popular.

In chapter one we considered how God has revealed himself in the other book of nature; committed Christians who have wanted to think God's thoughts after him have always been at the forefront of medical research. We now know a great deal more about the world than was known in Old or New Testament times and there are therefore approaches to health and healing operating rationally in response to new understandings of nature which were not available before. These are no less God-given than the supernatural approaches seen in the Bible and in Christian prayer for healing today. This chapter will mainly consider these natural approaches.

How were the early Christians different?

There had been strong medical traditions in the Buddhist, Jewish, Arab, Greek and Roman worlds but early on it is recorded that Christians had a radically different approach ethically. This began to change society's attitudes to the sick, the disabled and the dying. The first century world was a cruel one. The weak and the sick were looked down on and abortion, infanticide and killing by poisoning were widely practised. Doctors were often sorcerers as well as healers and alongside the power to heal they assumed a power to kill. Before the Christian church, only the Hippocratic physicians had a different attitude and had sworn their famous Oath accordingly, to heal and care for the sick and not to harm.

Clement was a Christian leader in Rome at the end of the first century and he recorded how the Christian church provided relief for widows. There is a striking example of Christian commitment in the second century. During an epidemic of plague in the city of Carthage, pagan households threw sufferers out onto the streets in order to protect themselves from infection. The bishop himself led the entire Christian community out into the open, comforting these unfortunates and taking them willingly into their own homes for care.

These examples occurred while Christianity was still an unofficial though fast growing phenomenon, but in AD 311 the Emperor Constantine granted the first Edict of Toleration and this official approval of the church allowed Christians publicly to express their ethical conviction. Their level of social service increased in terms of practical acts for the poor, orphans, widows, the elderly, prisoners and slaves. Perhaps they found inspiration from the New Testament letter of James: 'Religion that God our Father accepts as pure and faultless is this: to look after orphans and widows in their distress and to keep oneself from being polluted by the world' (James 1:27).

The Roman Emperor Julian came to power in 355 and was the last emperor to try to reinstitute paganism. In his Apology he noted that if the old religion wanted to succeed, its devotees would need to care for people better than the Christians cared.

How did hospitals and hospices develop?

Greek temples sometimes included areas where the sick could sleep in the hope of being visited by gods who might cure them, and I have sat in the remains of the temple of Asklepios on the island of Cos where Hippocrates (born 460 BC) is said to have practised. In fact very little is known about Hippocrates and there may well have been no one medical individual but a school of physicians responsible for the famous Oath.

From the Edict of Constantine onwards, Christian social concern led to the construction first of hospices (initially wayside dwelling places for weary travellers) and then of larger institutions called hospitals. In 369 St Basil of Caesarea founded a significant hospital, with wards caring for plague and leprosy patients, as well as chronic care facilities. In 375 St Ephraim founded a 300 bedded hospital for the plague stricken at Edessa. In Britain a number of monastic buildings which included hospices, elementary hospitals and herb gardens were established, examples being St Columba's, Iona (563) and St Cuthbert's, Lindisfarne (635).

The period between the fall of Rome in AD 476 and circa 1000 is known as the Dark Ages but rulers influenced by Christian principles encouraged hospital building. Charlemagne (742-814) decreed that every cathedral should have an attached hospital, monastery and school. In the later Middle Ages monks began taking care of the sick in infirmaries. Healthcare was originally for residents but larger monasteries developed separate buildings, which came to be called hospitals, and took in sick pilgrims and the more seriously ill in the neighbourhood. Concerned that this might distract monks from their spiritual duties, the Church banned monks from practising outside their monasteries and this move led to the training of lay physicians. Gradually cathedral cities began to provide more public hospitals and the church needed the support of secular authorities in this. Eventually most major cities and towns had a hospital.

During the Reformation (1536-1539) King Henry VIII closed monasteries and hospitals like St Bartholomew's and St Thomas's in London and this had a drastic effect on the care of the sick and the poor. Responsibility for health care became that of municipal City Fathers.

During the 18th century the Christian impetus for opening hospitals re-emerged because of the religious revival inspired by the preaching of men like John Wesley and George Whitefield. Realising that true Christian concern had to apply to body as well as to soul, a new *Age of Hospitals* began. These institutions were mainly intended for the sick poor and were supported by voluntary contributions. This influence was felt overseas as well, in continental Europe and in the New World, where Christian pioneers founded the first North American hospitals.

Eventually, Britain's National Health Service came in virtually overnight in 1948 and this monumental change in the delivery of healthcare was achieved partly by nationalising these voluntary hospitals. Britain now benefits from state-provided healthcare that is free at the point of delivery. The long history of different Christian contributions prior to nationalisation is often forgotten.

One of the great success stories of healthcare in the modern era has been the rediscovery of the old concept of a wayside dwelling place for the weary traveller in terms of providing appropriate care for the terminally ill. The highest standards of multidisciplinary professional care are applied to the physical, psychological, social and spiritual symptoms of terminal illness in a response to what has been called *total pain*. Initially Christian, and still with a very strong Christian element, there are now around 200 hospice buildings in the UK and many more palliative care teams and units. Palliative care is not about buildings though. It is a concept concerned with recognising the reality of approaching death and changing treatment goals so that we always care for patients even when we can no longer cure them. Palliative care is practised in general hospital wards and in patients' homes as well as in hospices, and the concept is rapidly catching on around the world.

How have Christians influenced primary health care?

Following the 18th century revival, Christians were pioneers in the development of the dispensary movement. Dispensaries could be regarded as the prototype for primary health care in that they provided medical treatment for the poor in what we now call inner city areas. During epidemics of cholera and other fevers, many large hospitals closed because of fear of infection. Just as in Carthage in the second century, there are examples of Christians motivated by compassion staying behind to keep small inner city dispensaries open.

Around the turn of the 19th – 20th century various inner city medical missions developed. Some have adapted and survive within the NHS today. I had the privilege of doing my ten years' general practice at what was then called the Brook Lane Medical Mission. This was an offshoot of the Bermondsey Medical Mission, which had been founded in 1904 in a tough dockland area of London. In the 1920s the worst of the Bermondsey slums began to be demolished. Whole streets of people were rehoused in new garden estates being built in what was then the Kent countryside, but which rapidly became part of the south east London sprawl.

In the recession of the early 1930s the breadwinner of the household, even if unemployed, would be covered by rudimentary insurance and would have a panel doctor, but there was no such provision for his wife and children. Women were regularly carrying children ten miles or so from these estates to Bermondsey to be treated almost free at the Bermondsey Medical Mission Hospital. This had grown from the earlier Mission and was one of those Christian charitable hospitals mentioned in the section above, which was to be nationalised on 5th July 1948. Because of the distress of these families, a single doctor and a single nurse from the hospital in Bermondsey came to be called by God to set up a primary care work, and went to one of the estates looking for premises.

They considered rooms above a fish and chip shop – and I am glad they rejected those as I don't think I could have lived with the smell of frying – but eventually settled in the back of a church hall and the practice has been there ever since. There have of course been a number of redevelopments, and today there is a fine modern health centre alongside attractive and functional church premises.

What is vocation?

Describing the pioneers of the practice where I worked I used the expression *called by God*. It is this concept of *call* that is behind the word vocation. Many health professionals, whether they had religious faith of any kind or not, would happily have accepted until quite recently that their work was a vocation. I have seen the concept of vocation disappear in Britain to the point where medicine is now seen as a profession, admittedly, but essentially as just a job. Whilst there is always a danger that altruism and idealism will be exploited, and I do not argue for one moment against the highest achievable standards of professionalism, I believe Christians should set an example and practise medicine as a vocation.

The embryonic 1937 general practice at Brook Lane was nationalised in 1948 and became part of the NHS, but in the greatly changed social circumstances after World War II new needs were becoming apparent. The doctors and nurses at Brook Lane Medical Mission identified the need for residential care for those who had been bombed out of their houses; by 1948 the Mission had moved into the business of old people's homes and nursing homes. In this they were much inspired by a single verse in the Psalms, 'God sets the lonely in families' (Psalm 68:6), although they knew it in the more poetic Authorised Version, 'God setteth the solitary in families'. This inspirational motif of relationship and community helped them through the tremendous struggles to raise funds, acquire suitable property and attract appropriate staff.

In a response to a perceived need several of the early nursing homes also began to take care of young people with chronic physical disabilities and for a while one of them also looked after the dying. Dr (now Dame) Cicely Saunders spent some time there while she was planning what was to become St Christopher's Hospice, the first hospice of the modern era.

Britain's state National Health Service is moving into ever more partnerships with the private and charitable sectors. The 100 year history of this particular Mission's development illustrates a number of examples of appropriate Christian response to need. Whilst other groups and individuals not motivated by Christian commitment may have done equally well or better, the church in Britain need not be too backward in coming forward about its historic involvement in health and healing.

How did overseas medical mission develop?

Like many questions in this book, this question deserves a book of its own; indeed, it has one – see *Heralds of Health* in *References and Further Reading*. In short, medical care was part of the great 19th century missionary enterprise and remains a key part today. Everybody knows about David Livingstone who worked in Central Africa and Albert Schweitzer who took his medicine, music and theology to the remote forests of Gabon. There are hundreds of others, doctors and nurses and other health professionals, who went abroad in the 19th and 20th centuries; although world conditions are changing fast, many still go today. The contexts may be different but the desire to serve those in need is still there.

There have been many changes in the countries the medical missionaries went to. Some now have thriving health services staffed entirely by locals and some still benefit from western staff going out to train and to provide services. Countries in the developing world by definition are poor. In chapter three, *What is health?* we considered the Christian obligation to work for fairer distribution of resources.

How have Christians responded to AIDS?

AIDS is one of the biggest threats to health in the world today and the pandemic shows no sign of abating. We saw in chapter four, *What is healing?* that leprosy (the biblical word covers a range of conditions with skin manifestations) affected sufferers physically, psychologically, socially and spiritually. We see Jesus touching people with this condition.

> *A man with leprosy came and knelt before him and said, "Lord, if you are willing, you can make me clean." Jesus reached out his hand and touched the man. "I am willing," he said. "Be clean!" Immediately he was cured of his leprosy. (Matthew 8:2-3)*

The touch was not just a symbol of the transmission of healing power but was also a symbol of identification with the sufferer despite ritual defilement, and therefore a symbol of welcome back into the community. Historically, leprosy has always attracted the concern of Christian health professionals, because of the medical need presented but perhaps too because of its whole person significance: cure can restore relationships. The biblical approach to leprosy is a paradigm for the Christian approach to AIDS.

After one or two shaky starts, Christians have become deeply engaged in the care of people with AIDS, in Britain and overseas. ACET (AIDS Care, Education and Training) is a huge charity providing care at home. The former Mildmay Mission Hospital in London's east end has become an AIDS hospice and has stimulated the development of similar hospices overseas.

The response to AIDS involves prevention in terms of health promotion, research into vaccines and drugs, and treatment of the sick. Here there is the familiar problem of poverty in that anti-retroviral drugs are expensive and often patients cannot afford the medication. The response to AIDS involves care for the dying and their families. Living a Christian lifestyle is powerfully protective: sexual faithfulness and avoidance of intravenous drug abuse promote good health, but around the globe Christians (and others of course) are providing non-judgmental care for those infected with HIV as professionally and as lovingly as possible.

Where else have Christians been involved in health and healing?

This chapter is not intended to be a long list, but there is no area of medicine or healthcare where Christians have not been involved and where they are not involved today. Christians are active in public health, preventative medicine and epidemiology; in all branches of clinical medicine; in research; in medical ethics and in medico-politics.

Most healthcare is delivered by professionals in disciplines other than medicine. Surely the most famous nurse of all time is Florence Nightingale who, returning to the concept of vocation, is reported to have said, 'God called me into his service, February 7 1837'. She encouraged better hygiene, improved standards, advocated night nursing and founded the first nursing school.

We saw in chapter three, *What is health?* that we must take a broad view of health and (politicians please note) one that crosses traditional boundaries in Whitehall. Overall, the single concept most closely associated with health is wealth, and response to poverty is part of healthcare. Dr Thomas Barnardo was a Christian who founded his homes for children after seeing their desperate needs in the east end of Victorian London. The Salvation Army is still the second largest provider of social care after the state, and helps health by giving many people more strength to be more human.

What made them do it?

Many Christians have received specific guidance for particular tasks through specific Bible verses. I mentioned Psalm 68:6 – 'God setteth the solitary in families' – in the context of residential homes. The Mission's rehabilitation work amongst people with disabilities was encouraged by a short extract from one of the letters to the seven churches in Revelation, 'Strengthen what remains' (Revelation 3:2).

However, there are more general verses which have inspired Christians over the years. Jesus was once asked which was the most important commandment?

> *"The most important one," answered Jesus, "is this: 'Hear, O Israel, the Lord our God, the Lord is one. Love the Lord your God with all your heart and with all your soul and with all your mind and with all your strength.' The second is this: 'Love your neighbour as yourself.' There is no commandment greater than these." (Mark 12:29-31)*

We considered the Great Commission in chapter five – 'Therefore go and make disciples of all nations…' (Matthew 28:19-20) – and these verses about love are often called the Great Commandment. Certainly, countless Christian medical missionaries have been inspired to go overseas by the Great Commission and the Great Commandment taken together. For Christians, healthcare is quite simply being obedient to the commandment, 'Love your neighbour'. We will consider what happened when somebody asked Jesus the obvious supplementary question, 'And who is my neighbour?' when we examine the lessons in the parable of the Good Samaritan in chapter eight.

Another well known verse is: 'In everything, do to others what you would have them do to you, for this sums up the Law and the Prophets' (Matthew 7:12). Some have called this the Golden Rule. Note that it is put in a positive sense, unlike the more popular (and non-biblical) version: 'Don't do to others what you wouldn't have them do to you!'

'He sent them out to preach the kingdom of God and to heal the sick' (Luke 9:2) has inspired many medical missionary works. Indeed the words are inscribed on the commemorative plaque for the recently opened joint health centre/church premises I mentioned earlier. I used the first four words as the title for my history of the Brook Lane Medical Mission.

Matthew 25:40 – 'Whatever you did for one of the least of these brothers of mine, you did for me' – comes half way through the parable of the sheep and the goats. This is one of the most challenging passages in the entire Bible. At the Judgment at the end of human history, two groups of outwardly similar people are separated on the basis of whether they did or did not feed the hungry, give the thirsty something to drink, invite in the stranger, clothe the needy, look after the sick or visit the prisoner. Those who did any or all of these did not realise they were doing it as to Jesus; conversely those who did not do any of these acts of service did not realise that, in neglecting to do them, they were neglecting Jesus himself. This concept is said to be the one that inspired Mother Teresa of Calcutta in her lifetime of service.

But you don't have to be a Christian to care?
No, of course you don't. Throughout history there have been many fine acts done by people of other religious faiths or of none. I remember being somewhat self-righteous at a young practitioners' discussion evening on ethics once and the expression, 'Speaking as a committed Christian...' slipped out. The very next speaker, an excellent GP, began his comments: 'Speaking as a committed atheist...'

Throughout history there have been many fine acts done by people of other religious faiths or of none, and sadly throughout history there have been many wrong acts done by people claiming to be Christians. None of this chapter, and certainly not the passages about my own modest work, is intended to be boastful. Boasting destroys the point of Christian service. But I sometimes think nowadays we are too apologetic about what Christians have achieved in the worlds of health and healing. Yes, many mistakes were made but many millions have been given more strength to be more human.

In chapter one, I mentioned that I became a Christian on evidence-based criteria, worn down by the weight of the evidence. I was at least equally inspired by what I saw of the life of Jesus Christ in the lives of some of my medical student colleagues. They had something I didn't have and I wanted it. That something was a commitment to service. It was to do with vocation. I end this chapter with another example of that commitment. During morning prayers, my senior partner – who had founded the mission practice 42 years earlier – always began her prayer, 'Lord, we thank you for another day in which to serve you'. Perhaps the National Health Service needs more of that commitment?

References and Further Reading

Beal-Preston R. The Christian Contribution to Medicine. *Triple Helix* 2000; Winter:9-14
ISSN 1460-2253
This is the postgraduate journal of the Christian Medical Fellowship (CMF). It can be seen on the *website* www.cmf.org.uk. Both Dr Beal-Preston and I drew on the following material:

Aitken JT, Fuller HWC, Johnson D. *The Influence of Christians in Medicine*. London: Christian Medical Fellowship, 1984
ISBN 0 906747 11 2

Browne SG (Ed). *Heralds Of Health – The Saga of Christian Medical Initiatives*. London: Christian Medical Fellowship, 1985
ISBN 0 906747 17 1

Fergusson A. *He Sent Them Out*. London: Bermondsey and Brook Lane Medical Mission, 1988
ISBN 0 9513534 0 3

7

What are Christians doing today?

What is happening in the National Health Service?

Chapter six brought us up to the present and much that I described continues. The UK National Health Service (NHS) employs over one million people and those of us who have worked or are working in the various Christian organisations for health professionals estimate that approximately ten percent of these are committed Christians. These 100,000 or so have an opportunity to express their faith quietly in good quality service, practising as a vocation in their paid professional work. This may involve some overt expression of faith or it may be in fulfilling the old adage attributed to St Francis of Assisi: 'Preach the gospel at all times and if necessary use words'.

Outside the health professions, there are several million lay carers in Britain looking after family members or, sometimes, neighbours. They may or may not receive social recognition and financial support, but without them health and social services in Britain could not begin to cope. Many of these lay carers are Christians but of course Christians do not have a monopoly on care. However, the challenge 'Love your neighbour' remains as strong in the lives of individuals today as it has always done.

What effect has whole person healthcare had?

We noted in chapters two and three that our understanding of what it means to be human influences our understanding of what health is, and that understanding in turn influences the way healthcare is performed. Scientific western medicine still tends to see human beings as bodies only, and therefore concentrates on cure of physical symptoms or pathology. Psychiatry and psychology are there separately for problems of the mind, though psychosomatic medicine recognises the inter-relation of mind and body.

However there is an ever-growing return to whole person healthcare. This is being seen particularly in primary care, not least with the rise and rise of alternative medicine. Also known as *complementary* or *holistic* medicine, it has been defined by Professor Ernst (Britain's first professor in the subject) as: 'Diagnosis, treatment and/or prevention which complements mainstream medicine by contributing to a common whole, by satisfying a demand not met by orthodoxy or by diversifying the conceptual frameworks of medicine'. Another more practical working definition would be that alternative medicine is anything not taught in the medical school curriculum! However, yesterday's alternative can be tomorrow's orthodoxy and a number of newer therapies previously seen as alternative are now accepted within mainstream medicine.

There has been a steady growth in this phenomenon over the last 20 years. In the year 2000, 40% of UK general practices offered at least one alternative therapy and greater use still was then expected. Much complementary/alternative medicine is practised in the private sector outside of general practice or hospitals, and one of many legitimate concerns is about the training and regulation of the therapists.

Nevertheless complementary/alternative medicine is a multi-million pound industry and many lay Christians have trained in one or more aspects and are active in private practice. Whilst an assessment of complementary/alternative medicine requires a book of its own (and indeed has one – see *References and Further Reading* at the end of the chapter), in the context of this book it is worth pausing to consider why it has become so popular.

Why is complementary/alternative medicine so popular?

I mentioned in chapter two, *What does it mean to be human?* that many aspects of the Christian worldview square with people's intuitions. The growing unease with orthodox medicine and the consequent rise and rise of the alternatives confirm the perception of many ordinary people that medicine does not understand or meet all their needs. Reasons for the popularity of complementary/alternative medicine include:

• **failures of orthodox medicine**
So successful has the reductionist technological approach been that patients understandably expect to be cured of every sickness. They expect a pill for every ill. Yet unless Jesus comes back first, we are all going to die one day and sooner or later, the time comes for all when orthodox medicine cannot hold out the promise of cure. In Britain, many first try alternative medicine for serious conditions when orthodox medicine is no longer effective.

• **medical arrogance**
Although communication skills are being taught much more (and, perhaps more importantly, are being tested in examinations) and bedside manner is improving, many patients recognise an unconscious arrogance in their doctors and nurses and prefer the way many alternative practitioners listen to them.

• **iatrogenic disease**
The word iatrogenic means caused by doctors. The other side of the coin is that many modern medical treatments with powerful beneficial effects have powerful side effects. Rarely these can even be fatal. By contrast, most complementary/alternative medicines are relatively harmless.

• **holism versus reductionism**
Patients intuitively recognise that they are more than bodies, more than a body/mind combination, and demand whole person medicine that acknowledges more of their felt needs.

• **costs**
High technology medicine is expensive. Most complementary/alternative medicines involve little more in the way of resources than the therapist's time, and are therefore by nature cheaper. This may be part of the explanation for the (sometimes too uncritical) acceptance of them into the NHS. Further, most expenditure on them takes place outside the NHS in the private sector, and the government probably welcomes this.

• **healthism**
We have noted in previous chapters the current idolatry of images of health. The alternative sector has tapped into that. This is not necessarily to accuse complementary/alternative practitioners of profiteering – in my experience most have the same sincere motivations as most orthodox practitioners and only want to help people.

• **spiritual dimension**
Many complementary/alternative medicine therapies are implicitly or explicitly spiritual. It is partly this phenomenon that

has led to spirituality being back officially on the government's healthcare agenda, but rather than being Christian the spirituality in question has often been New Age in origin. (For a description of the New Age and its association with alternative medicine, see *References and Further Reading* at the end of the chapter.) Christians should not over-react but be grateful for this rediscovery of spirituality within whole person healthcare, and be challenged to provide a genuinely Christian whole person care so that any counterfeits fade by comparison.

Finally in this brief consideration of the roles Christians do and do not play in complementary/alternative medicine, I often say to concerned Christian enquirers that I am not so much concerned about the nature of the therapy on offer as I am about the nature of the therapist. It is not so much 'What is this therapy?' as 'Who is this therapist?' There is always a great power imbalance between therapist and recipient and we see subconscious acknowledgement of this in the everyday expression, 'I'm under the doctor'. Perhaps the most important spiritual question is 'Who is this person I am placing myself under?' Perhaps that question should be asked of all practitioners whether they are orthodox or alternative.

What examples of whole person healthcare are there in hospitals?

Over recent years the quality of hospital chaplains has improved considerably. Maybe I am being cynical but I think at one time there was a tendency for failed parish clergy to be transferred to hospital chaplaincy where perhaps it was thought they could do less harm. Nowadays, chaplains are highly motivated, well trained and usually highly regarded by other members of the multidisciplinary hospital teams.

Chaplains themselves are often team leaders with trained hospital visitors working under them; together they are inspiring greater attention to spiritual care. The whole question of still closer co-operation will be examined further in the next chapter.

In chapter six we considered the origin of hospices as wayside dwelling places for the weary traveller, and their evolution into bigger and more specialised hospitals. The hospices of the modern era, whilst being established to care for the dying and develop the relatively new specialty of palliative care, have also taken a more spiritual view. For example, Dame Cicely Saunders pioneered the concept of *total pain* that includes spiritual pain.

What is happening in the churches?

The Church of England in 2000 published a substantial work called *A Time to Heal*, the first report from the Anglican church on the ministry of healing for over 40 years. This comprehensive report reviews the history of healing and the current state of the ministry of healing in the established church and in the other denominations. To its credit, the Church of England has maintained a balanced practical approach to Christian prayer for healing more consistently perhaps than other denominations, where fashions have come and gone. Even within the Church of England, the nature of any healing service will depend on the churchmanship and style of the individual church involved.

Pentecostal and charismatic churches place particular emphasis on practising the spiritual gifts we considered briefly in chapter five. Indeed, the word charismatic comes from the Greek for gifts. Christians disagree about the proper extent of this emphasis. I see myself as middle of the road, accepting the clear biblical statement, 'Now to each one the manifestation of the Spirit is given for the common good' (1 Corinthians 12:7). I believe the Bible tells us that each Christian has at least one spiritual gift, but it is there for the common good, to build up the church. I am not aware of possessing any of the more obviously supernatural gifts despite prayer over the years that God would give me what he wants me to have, though I do accept that some people possess these supernatural gifts. I think I know by now what my natural gifts are but trust I am not limiting God's continuing work in my life.

There has perhaps been a tendency in some sections of the church to emphasise the more spectacular supernatural gifts at the extent of the natural gifts. Interestingly, in a list in 1 Corinthians 12:28, gifts of healing comes between miracle workers (clearly supernatural) and those who help others including administrators (clearly natural). Perhaps that placement is deliberate!

Christians in all denominations and all sections of the church are subject to prevailing emphases and fashions. The charismatic churches of the 1970s and early 1980s had a primary distinctive interest in the supernatural gift of speaking in tongues, a unique personal language with which those so gifted can pray and worship. In the late 1980s and early 1990s interest was mainly in healing. Since the early 1990s it has been in the gift of *words of knowledge*, receiving supernatural communications directly from God. Some of these issues will be considered further in chapter twelve, *How should Christians pray for healing?* but I believe the church at large has moved on from an inappropriate over-emphasis on certain aspects of healing and that we are seeing less of the extremes of the Christian healing movement.

What extremes are there?

1. God does not heal supernaturally today

On the one hand are the Christians labelled dispensationalists who believe that because the New Testament documents had been delivered, the charismatic gifts ceased at the end of the apostolic era (by the end of the first century AD). They point out that Old Testament miracles were clustered in certain time periods, that the New Testament letters make almost no mention of healing and that there is little evidence from church tradition. Even though it is always dangerous to argue from silence, they therefore claim we should not expect miracles today. In particular, there is in any case no need to pray for healing any more because healthcare is provided by doctors and nurses and others employed by the state.

Those holding such views therefore do not pray for healing; so they do not see answers to prayer for healing. This reinforces their prior assumption that God does not heal today; so they don't pray for healing; and the cycle continues. Some commentators have used a paraphrase of the Beatitudes (Jesus' statements beginning 'Blessed are...' in Matthew 5:1-12) to sum up this position: 'Blessed are they who expect nothing for they shall not be disappointed'.

2. God always heals today provided we do it right

At the other extreme are those Christians who believe that healing is the right of every Christian. They answer the question, 'Is there healing in the atonement?' with an over-emphatic and over-literal, 'Always!' They believe we should pray for every condition rather than seek professional attention. If people are not healed immediately they offer explanations.

- **There is lack of faith**
  The patient, those who have brought him or those praying lack the necessary faith. Faith is of course involved and we will consider its role in chapter eleven, *Must you have faith to be healed?* but there is no magic faith formula. This grave error means that not only is the patient still sick, perhaps dying, but that he, his family and friends are further burdened by accusations of deficient or defective Christianity.

- **There is unconfessed sin**
  The patient is not healed because there is some sin in his life which he has not yet confessed to God. It is therefore not forgiven so he cannot be whole and so cannot be healed of this sickness. Sin can be the cause of sickness – see chapter nine – but not

necessarily. If there is any sin present the simplest confession will deal with it provided the confession is sincere. To make this accusation burdens patients. Depression often accompanies physical illnesses. If a depressed person is sent off to search his soul for unconfessed sin, he will probably find material to add to rather than relieve his psychological and spiritual burden.

• **There is a specific demon that has not yet been named or cast out** We will examine the relationship between the demonic and disease in chapter ten but I do not accept that, in the very rare event of possible demonic involvement, it is necessary to discover the specific name of any demon for a successful exorcism and subsequent healing.

I will argue in chapter twelve that both these extreme positions are wrong. God does heal today, both naturally through the activities of health professionals and supernaturally in answer to prayer. It is entirely proper for lay Christians and for Christian health professionals to pray for healing provided a number of guidelines for appropriate practice are met. However, God does not always cure, either immediately or in the longer term. There is not a faith formula to be found that will guarantee healing. God's ways are mysterious and whilst he always answers prayer, he does not necessarily do it in the way we would want. We need an adequate theology of suffering as well as an adequate theology of healing.

Do healing miracles happen today?

The answer to that question largely depends on how we define our terms. In chapter five I quoted the Collins English Dictionary (21st Century Edition, 2000) definition of a miracle as '**1** an event contrary to the laws of nature and attributed to a supernatural cause. **2** any amazing or wonderful event. **3** a marvellous example of something: *a miracle of engineering*'. Participants in the sometimes heated debate about miraculous healing are often using not the first but the second or third definitions listed. I believe strongly that we should reserve the word miracle for the first definition only – 'an event contrary to the laws of nature and attributed to a supernatural cause'. I believe that because that is the sense in which the Bible uses it – though in fact the Bible prefers the words signs and wonders. I believe that Christians should always be scrupulously accurate, avoiding the tendencies to exaggeration and hyperbole that characterise our advertising-based commercial culture. I believe that we should not trivialise the works of God. We should not use the word miracle lightly.

In chapter five we saw that there was a biblical gold standard for miracles. Those in the Old Testament, and those of Christ and the disciples in the New Testament had the following hallmarks:

- the conditions were obvious examples of gross physical disease;
- they were at that time incurable and most remain so today;
- physical means were almost never used;
- the cures were immediate;
- restoration was complete and therefore obvious;
- there were no recorded relapses;
- miracles regularly elicited faith.

These characteristics clearly describe the first category of the three dictionary definitions quoted: 'an event contrary to the laws of nature and attributed to a supernatural cause'.

Ten years or so ago visiting charismatic evangelists were making regular high profile claims for healing miracles and for a while these were regularly featured in the mainstream media. At that time several Christian Medical Fellowship doctors holding different views about the charismatic healing debate – and as usual I found myself in the middle – got together to consider such claims. One of us at that time had about 20 years' experience of investigating claims of healing miracles, and for a while others including myself joined him.

Can claims for healing miracles be assessed?

By focusing on the characteristics of that narrow first category it is possible to make an empirical consideration. It is possible to gather data in an objective and describable area so that anybody with that data can make a considered judgment. Once the story has been heard and any necessary medical information has been obtained with consent, the claims lay Christians make, almost always sincerely and with good intention, can be investigated. Some first line questions include:

- What was the medical version of the story?
- What was the precise nature of the diagnosis?
- At what time did recovery take place?
- Were any treatments being given at the same time?

A second level of questions may then need to be considered. For example, concerning the diagnosis:

- On what basis was the diagnosis made?
- How reliable were the tests performed?
- How reliable were the observers conducting the tests?

(Interpreting X-rays for example is sometimes not easy and inexperienced junior doctors may draw the wrong conclusions.)
- Have experts checked the results?
- Could there be other explanations for the results?

Generally speaking such enquiries are not difficult. They may be time consuming as correspondence goes to and fro and participants may decline to co-operate for a variety of reasons. Even then data can be set down, although we must be open about questions left unanswered. But with a rigorous commitment to honesty and acknowledging frankly when conclusions have to be tentative, the story can frequently be told in all the essential details so that individual investigators, whether medically qualified or not, are highly likely to draw the same conclusions.

What are the results of these assessments?

Ten years ago, between us, we did not find a single case that unequivocally satisfied our strict criteria for a biblical, category one miracle of healing. For me at least, that remains true today.

I believe God answers prayers for healing. There are some thrilling stories I could tell, as I know many could. Yet, if I confine myself to assessing contemporary claims to healing miracles as to whether they fall into the first category, I have to report that I have no evidence personal or otherwise of such miracles happening today.

If I am honest, all my own thrilling stories fall into the second and third dictionary categories: 'any amazing or wonderful event' or 'a marvellous example of something'. Ten years ago, all of us had such stories. We christened them *Tales of the unexpected,* after a television series of that title then in vogue, because they were well beyond what we would have expected as experienced doctors. Generally speaking, recoveries happened in a natural way but appeared to be accelerated, sometimes very considerably. Patients got better much quicker than our experience dictated they should have. We could confidently claim these were amazing or wonderful events or marvellous examples of an answer to prayer for healing, but they were not 'events contrary to the laws of nature' and therefore could not necessarily be 'attributed to a supernatural cause'.

Such may be *signs and wonders* where God has graciously given *significant* and *wonderful* answers to prayer, but they do not match up to the gold standard of biblical miracles and I must not pretend they do.

Do these definitions really matter?

Some Christians argue that I am splitting hairs. 'It doesn't matter if it is category two or three', they say. 'It still falls under the definition of a miracle in the dictionary.' I think it matters for the reasons I set out above, reasons that mainly concern truth. We belittle the works of God if we exaggerate or are economical with the truth. Our not-yet-Christian friends will be put off if we claim that which is not entirely true. God is so big. He doesn't need that kind of help.

But what effect does my confession that I have seen only category two and three answers to prayer have on me? Whilst some Christians may disagree, I do not believe that there is any biblical reason why we should not expect to see answers to prayer for healing at least as exciting as those in Christ's time. We have already read how Jesus told the disciples:

> *I tell you the truth, anyone who has faith in me will do what I have been doing. He will do even greater things than these, because I am going to the Father. And I will do whatever you ask in my name, so that the Son may bring glory to the Father. You may ask me for anything in my name, and I will do it.* (John 14:12-14)

Perhaps if I had more faith (and I am not ignoring my warning above about faith formulae) I would see more. A sober review of the medical realities before and after prayer inspires me to pray not less but more. I do not want to limit God, but still have to live with the tension between the *now* and the *not yet* we considered at length in chapter five. I still have to understand suffering. I still have to maintain the perspective of the future hope of heaven. I need to pray more but I also need to trust more, especially when the answers to prayer are not what I would want.

Why are there inappropriate claims for miracles of healing?

There are several different categories accounting for the different interpretations that lay and medically qualified Christians may hold. Some of them are easier for doctors to understand than lay people, but I hope the illustrations in the following will help.

- **Wrong diagnosis?**
  Medicine is an inexact business and often a doctor's diagnosis is only a working hypothesis. Patients and their families can have

too much confidence in the doctor's diagnosis and in any case, for whatever reason, they often pick up wrong information.

A patient suddenly developed a very severe headache and called his GP. A sub-arachnoid haemorrhage (a bleed into the membranes overlying the brain) was tentatively diagnosed. He was admitted to hospital where the physician reached the same working diagnosis. A lumbar puncture (removal of a sample of cerebrospinal fluid) was performed but the result was entirely normal, ruling out the diagnosis.

Meanwhile, the family had quite rightly got their church praying. The next morning the patient, fully recovered, was sent home. The church rejoiced. As the patient was now well, no follow up was arranged. For the next 20 years his family and church believed, sincerely and perfectly understandably, that a miracle had occurred.

The family could not be expected to understand that, had doctors been certain of the diagnosis, they would not have needed to perform the lumbar puncture. The hospital doctor was following the scientific method of testing his first hypothesis. Perhaps the family heard 'It may be a sub-arachnoid haemorrhage' as 'It is a sub-arachnoid haemorrhage'. Nor could they necessarily be expected to understand that the normal lumbar puncture effectively excluded the diagnosis. No definite diagnosis was ever made but the headache could have been a severe migraine.

Interestingly, when the facts were explained to the man's wife she still maintained that a miracle had occurred – before the lumbar puncture was performed. This is a speculation that cannot be tested. Because of the patient's full recovery, this particular claim certainly remains in the category of a wonderful answer to prayer, but almost certainly moves out of the category of miracle and into the category of a misunderstanding based on an initial wrong diagnosis.

• **Spontaneous remission?**
Vittorio Michelli developed an enormous malignant tumour of his pelvis that looked likely to kill him. In 1963 he made a pilgrimage to the Roman Catholic shrine at Lourdes where he reported feeling better. An X-ray taken four months later showed the sarcoma still eroding his pelvis, but over the next year he gradually recovered fully. His pelvis and hipbones remained distorted but with special footwear he was able to lead a full and active life. The healing was extraordinary, not least in the way his

bones remoulded an effective hip joint. The Medical Bureau of Lourdes, which follows commendably strict criteria, declared it a miracle (number 62).

However, by our strict criteria his recovery was neither immediate nor complete. It did not coincide with his pilgrimage, although he felt better at the time. Similar remodelling of the hipbones has been documented elsewhere. It is more likely that this was a case of spontaneous remission. Of course, this phrase is just one that reminds us that doctors do not know everything, but lay Christians should not sneer at it either. Vittorio Michelli enjoyed a significant and wonderful answer to prayer, but it was only a partial healing, in the category two or three definition of miracle, not category one.

- **Hysteria?**

This label is used much less often in medicine now, but in the strict medical sense of the word it is a condition where at an unconscious psychological level patients mimic a physical illness. They are not doing this consciously or deliberately for gain – that would be malingering or fraud. Nor has a psychological cause led to an actual physical problem as in psychosomatic illness.

Just as the cause has been triggered at an unconscious psychological level, so the psychological mechanism may be reset suddenly in answer to prayer and the patient may improve dramatically and instantly. This may well be significant and wonderful in itself, but again it does not meet the biblical gold standard.

- **Psychosomatic illness?**

Here an actual physical condition has a psychological cause. A sudden improvement would be put down by most of us to natural psychological phenomena rather than to supernatural factors. This does not make recovery any the less welcome. If prayer has taken place, such a healing would certainly represent an exciting answer to prayer.

- **Misunderstanding?**

This category is the most common and there is often overlap with other categories.

A patient went to a doctor about his hiatus hernia and (some years ago now) a barium swallow X-ray was arranged. The report described an odd appearance in the pharynx, thought to be a cyst. We do not know what was said in the patient's presence but perhaps the scratching of heads and puzzled expressions spoke louder than words. The man concluded that the doctors had found the cause of his problem and that it was a tumour.

He was referred to an ENT specialist for a further opinion.

A group of friends prayed before the ENT appointment. Imagine the man's relief when the specialist examined him and said that he couldn't find anything wrong. As far as the patient was concerned, it was a miracle; doctors know it is quite common for special tests to mislead us with odd results. Had the cyst existed, it would have been unrelated to his presenting problem anyway. Interestingly, the patient continued to believe he had been healed miraculously even though he had to watch his diet and frequently took antacids.

- **Exaggerations, half truths, lies?**
The truth can often be the victim of enthusiasm. Perhaps this happens particularly in claims of miraculous healing. Some mean well and wish to glorify God. Yet, like the fisherman's catch, their stories grow in the telling. Others may have more worrying motives. At the extreme, outright fraud has been shown to have been committed by a TV evangelist in the USA.

What about trials of prayer for healing?

There have been attempts at controlled scientific trials of the efficacy of prayer for healing. For example, a TV programme screened in 2003 reported a three-year trial of the effects of prayer on 750 cardiac patients undergoing angioplasty in the USA for coronary heart disease. It purported to be a randomised double blind controlled trial where half the patients were randomly selected by computer to be prayed for but the other half would not receive organised prayer.

There are methodological concerns but the theology is arguably more troubling. The praying groups were recruited from around the world, not just from different Christian traditions but also from Jewish, Muslim, Buddhist and Hindu sources. In addition to this complicating inter-faith aspect, the Bishop of Durham argued that both Old and New Testament teach that we should not put God to the test. He is not a slot machine we put our money into to get a chocolate bar out at the bottom. Perhaps the best line came from a patient without religious faith who reluctantly entered the trial and did receive prayer. On hearing that half the patients would be prayed for and half would not, to see if God answered prayer, he protested: 'What kind of a God is that? I want a God who loves us all'.

For what it is worth, there was no evidence that prayer made any difference to the physical outcomes measured in the trial. The group receiving prayer may have felt less distress during the actual intervention and may have had a greater sense of well-being afterwards. There have been other smaller trials. I mention this particular one because of its size, its apparent scientific respectability, the publicity it achieved and because it highlights so well the theoretical and practical difficulties of putting God to the test.

So where do we go from here?

I have just made clear (and will emphasise again in chapter twelve) that this uncertain trial outcome and the catalogue of alternative explanations for miracles should not stop us praying for healing. However, it should make us cautious about the language we use in describing answers to prayer.

We need a more effective dialogue between the church and health professionals. The Church of England Report *A Time to Heal* rightly notes that now is a time of great opportunity for developing a balanced approach to the Christian healing ministry in association with professional healthcare. In the next chapter we turn to this opportunity.

References and Further Reading

A Time to Heal. London: Church House Publishing, 2000
ISBN 0 7151 3837 5

Coker R. *Alternative Medicine: Helpful or Harmful?* Crowborough: Christian Medical Fellowship/Monarch, 1995
ISBN 1 85424 324 1
For discussion about the New Age, see pages 34-36 and 85-89.

Ernst E et al. Complementary medicine – a definition. *British Journal of General Practice*, 1995; 45:506

Everyman – Does Prayer Work? London: BBC2, 2003; 23rd October

8

Can health professionals and the church work together?

I have stated in this book that I would like to bridge the gap between healthcare as practised by health professionals and healing as practised by Christians in the churches. I have written this book because I believe that traditional biblical Christian understandings of what it means to be human (and therefore what health, healing and healthcare are) would have an enormously beneficial effect on health in the UK if they could cross over into the National Health Service (NHS).

That word service is an interesting one. Working in the NHS is vocational or it should be. It is a form of service. Christians may hear an echo of Mark 10:45: 'For even the Son of Man did not come to be served, but to serve, and to give his life as a ransom for many'. So can those who serve through the church and those who serve in the NHS (whether they realise that is what they are doing or not) ever work together?

What has happened historically?

In chapter six we saw that from the beginning of the history of what we now call healthcare, religion has always been closely linked with it. We saw the dramatic impact of the early Christian church's view of what it meant to be human on the way they treated the sick and dying. We saw how Christians founded hospices (initially wayside dwelling places for the weary traveller) and later hospitals in close association with churches and cathedrals. We saw how during the 18th century the Christian impetus for opening hospitals re-emerged because of religious revival, and how Christians were pioneers in the development of the dispensary movement, the prototype for primary health care in inner city areas. Right up until Britain's NHS came in virtually overnight in 1948, there were many examples of overt links between church and professional healthcare. Now this long history of different Christian contributions is often forgotten.

What is happening now?

We are currently recovering from the worst ravages of reductionism. Philosophically, this approach examined the biblical concept of human beings as a whole of body, mind and spirit, and then decided that if the spirit existed, the church could deal with it. Body and mind were then separated, so to speak, and medical science focused in ever closer on the physical units and subunits of the body. Scientific reductionism has of course led to many wonderful medical advances. The approach is fine as far as it goes but we always need to remember that it may not go far enough.

Psychosomatic medicine started to put mind and body back together. As we noted in chapters two and three, a more holistic understanding of humanity is growing as a cultural phenomenon and has led many more people to acknowledge spiritual aspects of health. However, despite the cultural conditions again becoming ripe for a synthesis, there are few obvious links between Christian spirituality and professional healthcare any longer.

What could happen in the future?

Could the concept of partnership develop?

The cultural conditions are ripe for a new synthesis in healthcare between the spiritual and the scientific. There are other favourable phenomena too. Partnership is a popular concept in many walks of life: at an individual level, partnership is coming into vogue in healthcare.

I qualified in 1975 at the height of the era of medical paternalism. Doctors still gave doctor's orders and I once heard Sister tell a patient, 'Doctor is always right!' Since then, and properly, the pendulum has swung. But it has now swung too far to the other extreme. Patient autonomy (self determination) knows no limits. In a litigation culture we hear all about patients' rights without ever hearing about their responsibilities and the restrictions that we must therefore all accept.

Rather than either of these extremes, healthcare should be practised, in Dr David Cook's words, as a dialogue between two experts. These two experts are the doctor or nurse, who is an expert in her own specialty, and the patient, who is an expert in two things, how he feels and what he wants. The most ethical and effective decisions are made out of this dialogue of two experts.

This concept of a partnership between two individuals can be extended into bigger partnerships still. In this understanding is fertile ground for health professionals and the church to work more closely together.

Could multidisciplinary teams be extended?

Another feature of the delivery of healthcare in my professional lifetime has been the growing importance of multidisciplinary teams, both in hospitals and in the community. Could more lay people be added to those teams? What expanded role might there be for the hospital visitors who serve under chaplains? What parallel role might there be in the community?

The opportunity in teamwork is there because of the importance of relationships, one aspect of the image of God that we have seen as a motif throughout this book. When talking about the church (in the sense of a community of believers rather than the large institutions that now exist), the Bible uses the metaphor of the inter-relationships between the organs in the human body:

> *Just as each of us has one body with many members, and these members do not all have the same function, so in Christ we who are many form one body, and each member belongs to all the others. (Romans 12:4-5)*

This exciting sense of inter-dependence and mutual service is difficult to understand in our individualistic western culture where autonomy and independence are so prized, but community has to be rediscovered if we are to have healthier societies.

What possibilities might there be?

This has to be speculative but the church could help professionals:

- **in fundamental concepts**

   The Christian understanding of what it means to be human affects our understanding of what health is, and therefore what healing and healthcare should involve. Nowhere in the world, no matter how rich or poor the countries in question, are the resources thought to be enough. Whilst some countries genuinely need more resources, others might benefit from a rigorous re-evaluation of priorities that could follow a new understanding of health. If the supply-demand equation is always going to be politically unsatisfactory because supply can never be great enough, might perhaps society one day re-evaluate the demand side of the equation?

- **in health promotion**

  The real successes of Western healthcare have not so much come from curative medicine as from preventative medicine, and not so much even from what is traditionally understood as preventative medicine as from taking a much broader view of health. For example, better nutrition and housing, clean water and sewage disposal, safer workplaces and transport have led to huge health benefits. Health promotion involves encouraging and facilitating healthier lifestyle choices.

  There is one area of behaviour where Christian concepts, if followed, could have a massively beneficial effect on health – the whole area of sexuality. There are pandemics of sexually transmitted infections, some of which are fatal, cause incurable distressing symptoms or lead to infertility with all its consequent suffering. Curiously, if doctors ever suggest that people amend their sexual habits, they are accused of moralising. But all they are doing is passing an objective judgment on the adverse health consequences of behavioural choices. Doctors do that all the time in other areas: 'Stop smoking! Eat less! Drink less alcohol! Exercise more!' If they failed to give this advice they would be guilty of negligence. So why can we not give public health consideration to a healthier message about sexual choices? Why can we not appropriately raise those issues with individual patients?

  A confident church could present such messages; whilst earning the right to be heard by offering non-judgmental care for those affected by the conditions in question, it could have a really positive impact in health promotion.

- **in practical care**

  The delivery of healthcare in the UK depends on the commitment of several million voluntary carers. There must be a great potential role for Christians in local churches to help more in practical ways at community level.

What issues would arise?

If such proposed partnerships and multidisciplinary teams are to develop, and the church is to have greater influence on the thinking and the practice of health professionals, then the practical issues are going to be around boundaries and overlap.

- **training**

  Nobody doubts that health professionals need training. I suggest in chapter twelve, *'How should Christians pray for healing?'* that prayer for healing should be led by experienced and responsible people, who themselves train others. Christian healing does not need to become too professional but it does need to be done properly. The churches cannot expect health professionals to take them seriously unless they show equivalent degrees of responsibility.

- **qualifications**
In healthcare these follow the approval of training. Without making everything too formal, the church should consider ways of recognising ability, training and experience.

- **protocols and guidelines**
Many experienced health professionals may feel there are too many of these in clinical use today; but for the new practitioner or for someone meeting a new and unfamiliar problem, they can be very helpful. The danger of protocols is that some people do everything by the book, ticking boxes either literally or metaphorically in order to cover themselves; in doing so, they cease to think originally. With this caveat, there may be a place for protocols and guidelines for lay Christians involved in healthcare.

- **audit and critical incident analysis**
In an era of evidence based medicine, health professionals are used to these concepts. Audit is about collecting evidence and learning from it. Critical incident analysis is about learning from mistakes. Again, the church might find things worth copying in these concepts.

- **up to date?**
In any health discipline and its various subspecialties, more and more is being learned and applied all the time and staying up to date is difficult. This is part of the reason why there are fewer and fewer generalists and ever more specialists. There is no obvious equivalent in Christian service; quoting Hebrews 13:8, 'Jesus Christ is the same yesterday and today and for ever'. Still, if Christian spirituality were to be practised within mainstream healthcare, there would be an obligation to stay in touch with developments of mutual relevance.

- **confidentiality**
Confidentiality is a vital concept in both professional and church life, and anybody involved in healthcare must be fully aware of its importance. In my experience Christian church leaders are more careful than health professionals regarding confidentiality. Church and health professionals would have to have mutual respect for each other's standards and safe systems in order to be able to work more closely.

- **communication**

  One of the dangers within multidisciplinary teams is failure of communication. If teams were enlarged, then communication (balanced by confidentiality) would become more important still. Good communication is needed with the patient, his family and within the team.

- **respect**

  I suggest in chapter twelve that prayer for healing should be patient-centred and that the patient should be accorded maximum respect. Does the church have something to teach health professionals here?

  As I have written these comments about possible practical issues if church and health professions are to work more closely together, I am struck that they will be very familiar, perhaps tediously so, to most health professionals. I suspect they will be relatively new to many lay Christians. We will have to learn something of each other's language. As I suspect that any closer working together, if it happens, will start from the church's side rather than that of the monolithic NHS, I commend these concepts for consideration.

What are the hallmarks of holistic healthcare?

Luke was a doctor and he alone records the well-known Parable of the Good Samaritan. Parables are stories with a hidden meaning that have one central message to convey – in this case, that our neighbour is anybody whom God brings us into contact with – but we should beware drawing too many conclusions from the details. However, the Parable of the Good Samaritan is so obviously about healthcare that it is worth seeing if there are any general principles that might guide health professionals and the church in working together.

> *On one occasion an expert in the law stood up to test Jesus. "Teacher," he asked, "what must I do to inherit eternal life?" "What is written in the Law?" he replied. "How do you read it?" He answered: "'Love the Lord your God with all your heart and with all your soul and with all your strength and with all your mind'; and, 'Love your neighbour as yourself'." "You have answered correctly," Jesus replied. "Do this and you will live." But he wanted to justify himself, so he asked Jesus, "And who is my neighbour?"*
>
> *In reply Jesus said: "A man was going down from Jerusalem to Jericho, when he fell into the hands of robbers. They stripped him of his clothes, beat him and went away, leaving him half-*

dead. A priest happened to be going down the same road, and when he saw the man, he passed by on the other side. So too, a Levite, when he came to the place and saw him, passed by on the other side. But a Samaritan, as he travelled, came where the man was; and when he saw him, he took pity on him. He went to him and bandaged his wounds, pouring on oil and wine. Then he put the man on his own donkey, brought him to an inn and took care of him. The next day he took out two silver coins and gave them to the innkeeper. 'Look after him,' he said, 'and when I return, I will reimburse you for any extra expense you may have.'

"Which of these three do you think was a neighbour to the man who fell into the hands of robbers?" The expert in the law replied, "The one who had mercy on him."

Jesus told him, "Go and do likewise." (Luke 10:25-37)

There are five key principles in the details of this passage that give us hallmarks for whole person healthcare:

- **comprehensive compassion:** *'...a Samaritan...took pity on him.'*
The priest and the Levite, both of whom had religious obligations to help but probably used their religious concerns about defilement as an excuse, passed by on the other side. The original hearers would have been shocked to discover that the Samaritan, hated at the time by the Jews, was the one who cared. Our compassion must extend to all and therefore cross all religious, racial and traditional boundaries.

   The opening of the parable also brings out implications for taking a broad view of health. The fact that a mugging happened on a poorly policed road reminds us of the effects of crime and social conditions on health.
- **costly commitment:** *'He went to him...'*
There was physical risk for the Samaritan as he went out of his way. For all he knew, the body was a decoy. There is often physical risk today for health professionals. For example, risk of infection with HIV; in 2003 we have seen significant numbers of health professionals dying after being infected in the SARS epidemic. If the cost is not the potential one of mortality (death), it may be the potential of physical or psychological morbidity (harm). Being a health professional is stressful.

   Taking the concept of costly commitment more metaphorically, there are political implications for taxation and funding of health services. In the crude saying, if we want better healthcare, are we as a society prepared to put our money where our mouth is?

- **conscientious competence:** '*...and bandaged his wounds, pouring on oil and wine.*'
  The Samaritan gave him the best healthcare available in terms of knowledge at that time and available resources. Although we have considered the importance of practical issues like the training and qualifications of professionals, competence is not enough. We must always practise conscientiously, whatever our calling.

- **continuing care:** '*Look after him...and when I return, I will reimburse you for any extra expense you may have.*'
  No health service manager anywhere in the world today would give such an open-ended commitment financially. Yet this extract does highlight the importance of continuing care. As western societies change demographically, becoming older, there is going to be a greater burden, both financial and practical, in caring for the elderly.

  The enormous challenge of long-term care in the community gives the church a real opportunity to demonstrate neighbourly love.

- **Christ's commendation:** '*Go and do likewise.*'
  Jesus' statement effectively commends the Samaritan. For us, it raises these questions: 'Do we want commendation from the lips of Jesus? What motivates us? What really motivates health professionals, even Christian ones? What motivates lay Christians in the healing ministry?'

  We should be seeking Christ's commendation as our primary reward, whatever secondary financial rewards or marks of recognition may come our way.

So, can it happen?

My own limited experience of trying to bring health professions and church together is not encouraging. But I really do believe the opportunity is with us for a while. There should be attempts made to bring this about organisationally but it is more likely to happen as a consequence of local individual enterprises. I have indicated that I think the initiative is more likely to come from the church. If it does happen, the church and health professions working even more effectively together could stimulate a massive re-think by government of what health is and how the health service should be structured and funded. It would also be a powerful witness for Christ!

References and Further Reading

A Time to Heal. London: Church House Publishing, 2000
ISBN 0 7151 3837 5
Chapter five, *The Healing Ministry in Professional Health Care Settings* and chapter six, *The Healing Ministry and Professional Care Provision in the Parishes* are particularly relevant.

Parker R, Fraser D, Rivers D. *In Search of Wholeness – a Christian theology of healing and practical training for church and medical settings.* Nottingham: St John's Extension Studies/Acorn Christian Foundation, 2000
ISBN 1 900920 09 3
Unit seven, *Working in the Overlap* seeks to bridge the worlds of church and professional healthcare.

9

Does sin cause disease and death?

What is sin?

Sin is a piece of Christian jargon and neither the word itself nor the concept are popular nowadays. That is partly why I did not use the word in the *What do Christians believe?* account in chapter one, a written version of the typical approach I use when opening a discussion with a group of health professionals. However, I could not and did not duck the concept.

We are all made in the image of God...and are meant to have a relationship with him.

However, it is in our nature to do wrong sometimes and by the wrong choices each of us makes we cut ourselves off from God and our relationship with him; hence our relationships with other people and the environment are spoiled.

I chose that language because I wanted to emphasise the importance of relationships in every area of human life, especially healthcare, and to confirm that as ethical beings made in the image of God, we have the capacity to make moral choices and we do so. Unfortunately, many of the choices we make are wrong.

In chapter two, *What does it mean to be human?* we considered the second theological pillar of the Fall. We saw how God gave the perfect world of Eden to Adam and Eve to enjoy, to reproduce in and fill, but then we met the serpent who '...was more crafty than any of the wild animals the Lord God had made'. He is a symbol of evil and tempted first Eve and then Adam to disobey God. The mistakes of Adam and Eve are typical of all sins since, all mine and all yours. The essence of all sin is putting human judgment above divine command. Actions have consequences and through the whole creation being cursed, the Fall brought in its wake suffering and death. These are realities we all accept and expect, much as we would like to avoid them. This is the world we live in.

Sins have consequences; although through confession and repentance we can, by God's grace (his unmerited giving), find his forgiveness and make a new start, we may well have to live with the consequences of our sins. Tragically, all too often, these are in the area of health.

There are different reasons why we sin. The Church of England's liturgy (written aid for worship) lists '...through ignorance, through weakness, through our own deliberate fault'. I daily have to plead guilty on all three counts! The same liturgy talks of sins against God '...in thought, in word, and in deed' and reminds us that we can sin '...in the evil we have done and in the good we have left undone'. When we acknowledge that the concept of sin includes our thoughts and the things we know we should have done but did not do, I am sure that every honest person whatever their religious beliefs must admit that they sin.

Disagreement comes in assessing the seriousness and significance of sin. Some shrug and say, 'So what? I'm only human'. Precisely! We need to look at the problem from God's point of view. We need to remember that sin is pathological, a pathology with mortality (it kills) and morbidity (it damages health). Although it is God's diagnosis initially, when we come to recognise it ourselves, we need to apply the appropriate treatment. As I explained in chapter one, there is only one treatment.

> *God is love and wants the best for us, so he has to resolve this problem we have created. He sends his son to earth to show us how to live, to teach, to perform miracles, but ultimately he sends him to die on the cross. In this way the penalty a holy and just God requires for our wrong choices can be met...*

> *If I respond by turning away from the wrong way of living, by thanking God that the penalty for my wrong choices has been met by Christ's death on the cross, by acknowledging that God has confirmed his power in raising Jesus from the dead, and by committing myself from now on to living for Christ, then I know a new life. I know that new life here on earth, both naturally through the deep sense of peace that comes from realising God's forgiveness, and supernaturally through God's presence as he comes to live within me through his Holy Spirit. I will know that new life in heaven and can be certain of being with God eternally when I die, not because of what I have done but because of my faith in what Jesus has done....*

If I ignore God, either passively and apathetically, or in active rebellion and rejection, then by my own choice I will not know that new life now on earth either naturally or supernaturally. If I continue to ignore God up to the end of my life then one day God will have to say 'I'm sorry, I don't know you. You didn't want to know me. I can't let you into my heaven' and I will forever be separated from God in hell.

Around the time I became a Christian 30 years or so ago, I remember being challenged by a chapter in *My God is Real* by the late David Watson. He asked if sin was a Christian neurosis. Well, Christians can indeed get neurotic about it, but sin is more than that. It is a real diagnosis of a real pathology that has enormous significance for healthcare, and I make no apology for the length of this introduction. We cannot consider the health effects of sin unless we understand what it is.

Does sin directly cause disease and death?

It is immediately obvious that some specific diseases and conditions are directly caused by sinful choices. Examples include:

- the drinker whose liver failure is caused by over-consumption of alcohol
- the driver who causes a fatal collision because of excessive speed
- the husband with a sexually transmitted infection acquired after adultery
- the addict with AIDS because of intravenous drug abuse

These are examples of direct cause and effect links. Actions have consequences. That is the way the world is: 'Do not be deceived. God cannot be mocked. A man reaps what he sows' (Galatians 6:7).

In chapter three I mentioned that the Christian Medical Fellowship's *Affirmation on Christian Ethics in Medical Practice* emphasises in relation to patients that we should '…give effective service to those seeking our medical care irrespective of age, race, creed, politics, social status or the circumstances which may have contributed to their illness'. It matters not whether sin has caused their disease; patients should be treated effectively, compassionately and non-judgmentally. This is the outworking of the old Christian cliché, *hate the sin but love the sinner*.

Does sin indirectly cause disease and death?

As we saw in chapter two, *What does it mean to be human?* in a general sense, Adam's sin caused disease and death to enter the world. Paul comments on this concept in his letter to the church in Rome; he compares and contrasts Adam and Christ: 'For if, by the trespass of the one man, death reigned through that one man, how much more will those who receive God's abundant provision of grace and of the gift of righteousness reign in life through the one man, Jesus Christ' (Romans 5:17).

When God said to Adam, 'Cursed is the ground because of you' (Genesis 3:17), he was announcing a fracture in the relationship between Adam and his environment. In a sense, we remain at war with our environment today and disease is ever present. I find this idea difficult to comprehend fully, and – as in many medical areas of partial knowledge – resolve to accept what we do know and get on. That's the way it is.

In chapter 13, *Why does God allow suffering?* this theological explanation will be examined a little further; though, in my clinical and pastoral experience, I have never found complex theological explanations necessary. I have never found anybody surprised by the fact of disease and death. It is such a common part of our history and experience that we all expect it sooner or later. That's the way it is. People may be shocked, frightened and angry – but they are not surprised. In a general sense, sin is ultimately responsible for the existence of disease and death.

When we come to consider specific situations where, unlike the cause-and-effect examples given above, the relationship is not obvious, then the questions become much harder. Has sin caused this disease? Has sin caused this death? The Bible's answer to these questions is that yes, sin does specifically cause disease and death but by no means always. Every case is different.

Are there cases in the Bible where sin has not caused disease or death?

Yes. The book of Job in the Old Testament, which we will consider further in chapter thirteen, concerns suffering (including disease) that Job cannot understand, but which his friends put down to sin on his part. At the end of the book, God himself speaks and makes it clear that in the case of Job they are wrong.

Chapter nine of John's gospel details the healing by Jesus of a man blind from birth, and all the aftermath of that healing. In verse two we hear the hard question: 'His disciples asked him, "Rabbi, who sinned, this man or his parents, that he was born blind?"' The disciples were betraying a common assumption of their time that suffering was caused by sin; the only question therefore was whether the individual or his parents were responsible.

Jesus' reply (verse three) is interesting: '"Neither this man nor his parents sinned...but this happened so that the work of God might be displayed in his life"'. Jesus then restored the man's sight and later he came to worship Jesus as Lord (verse 38). He was truly made whole.

I cannot resist recounting a poignant parallel with this case that I came across many years ago in general practice. When I met them, the happily married couple were in their 70s. They had both been born blind – although one had minimal perception of light and dark – and had met each other as teenagers in a home for the blind. The cause of their blindness was congenital syphilis, a sexually transmitted infection that is excluded nowadays by routine antenatal testing so we should never see such cases again. Each of their mothers had been infected with syphilis by sexual intercourse and had passed the infection on to their babies in the womb. (This parental involvement contrasts of course with the account in John's gospel.)

I don't think I had two more gracious patients. They had lived long and fulfilling lives, had been gainfully employed, and had raised a healthy family of their own. They put up with their visual and other disabilities patiently.

I don't think I had a more happily married couple on my list. The wife was the one who could just perceive light and she would walk in front. Her husband followed in step behind with his hands on her shoulders. One day in early spring I was driving on my rounds, some way from their sheltered accommodation, when I passed them. Their progress as usual was difficult but what so impressed itself on me and remains one of my most vivid memories was the expression of pure joy on their faces. They were revelling in the warmth of the spring sunshine, the gentle breeze and the smell of the flowers. They were very glad to be alive.

I said in chapter three, *What is health?* that some of my patients with gross medical problems were actually far more whole than I was, and in different ways taught me a great deal. These were two of them, perhaps the healthiest people on my list. In a paradoxical way, the work of God was displayed in their lives.

There is another example where Jesus makes it clear that sin was not the cause of suffering. It concerns a natural disaster: '"Or those eighteen who died when the tower in Siloam fell on them – do you think they were more guilty than all the others living in Jerusalem?"' Jesus then turns consideration of that tragedy into a spiritual warning: '"I tell you, no! But unless you repent, you too will all perish."' (Luke 13:4-5)

So, we know that disease and death are not necessarily caused directly by sin. Those over-zealous believers in Christian healing we considered in chapter seven are rarely if ever right when they explain somebody's lack of healing by saying that the condition in question was caused by a sin which has not been specifically confessed.

Are there cases in the Bible where sin has caused disease or death?

Yes. There are clear warnings in the Bible and we will look at a few.

The Old Testament

In the Old Testament book of Numbers, there is a record of God rebuking Aaron and Miriam for sinfully criticising his special messenger, their brother Moses:

> *"Why then were you not afraid to speak against my servant Moses?" The anger of the Lord burned against them, and he left them. When the cloud lifted from above the Tent, there stood Miriam – leprous, like snow. Aaron turned towards her and saw that she had leprosy; and he said to Moses, "Please, my lord, do not hold against us the sin we have so foolishly committed. Do not let her be like a stillborn infant coming from its mother's womb with its flesh half eaten away." So Moses cried out to the Lord, "O God, please heal her!" The Lord replied to Moses, "If her father had spat in her face, would she not have been in disgrace for seven days? Confine her outside the camp for seven days; after that she can be brought back." So Miriam was confined outside the camp for seven days, and the people did not move on until she was brought back. (Numbers 12:8b-15)*

Reading this with modern eyes, we may feel uncomfortable, but it illustrates a holy God's diagnosis of sin which is belatedly recognised by Aaron (and presumably Miriam, who was probably more to blame), his temporary punishment of a disease affecting the skin (not necessarily leprosy), and the seven day limit God set upon his discipline. The direct link between the sin and the medical problem is clear.

The Old Testament also describes a similar infliction on King Uzziah, though in his case the disease persisted until his death:

> *But after Uzziah became powerful, his pride led to his downfall. He was unfaithful to the Lord his God, and entered the temple of the Lord to burn incense on the altar of incense. Azariah the priest with eighty other courageous priests of the Lord followed him in. They confronted him and said, "It is not right for you, Uzziah, to burn incense to the Lord. That is for the*

priests, the descendants of Aaron, who have been consecrated to burn incense. Leave the sanctuary, for you have been unfaithful; and you will not be honoured by the Lord God."

Uzziah, who had a censer in his hand ready to burn incense, became angry. While he was raging at the priests in their presence before the incense altar in the Lord's temple, leprosy broke out on his forehead. When Azariah the chief priest and all the other priests looked at him, they saw that he had leprosy on his forehead, so they hurried him out. Indeed, he himself was eager to leave, because the Lord had afflicted him.

King Uzziah had leprosy until the day he died. He lived in a separate house – leprous and excluded from the temple of the Lord. (2 Chronicles 26:16-21)

These two examples both concern individuals. There are also warnings to whole populations about what will happen if they continue to sin against God:

However, if you do not obey the Lord your God and do not carefully follow all his commands and decrees I am giving you today, all these curses will come upon you and overtake you:...The Lord will plague you with diseases until he has destroyed you from the land you are entering to possess. The Lord will strike you with wasting disease, with fever and inflammation, with scorching heat and drought, with blight and mildew, which will plague you until you perish. (Deuteronomy 28:15, 21-22)

The Old Testament makes it clear that sin can directly cause disease and death.

The New Testament

There are also examples in the New Testament where sin directly causes disease and death. During the very early days of the church, and probably as a necessary salutary warning to the new Christians, we read in Acts of the related deaths of Ananias and Sapphira:

Now a man named Ananias, together with his wife Sapphira, also sold a piece of property. With his wife's full knowledge he kept back part of the money for himself, but brought the rest and put it at the apostles' feet.

Then Peter said, "Ananias, how is it that Satan has so filled your heart that you have lied to the Holy Spirit and have kept

> *for yourself some of the money you received for the land?*
> *Didn't it belong to you before it was sold? And after it was*
> *sold, wasn't the money at your disposal? What made you think*
> *of doing such a thing? You have not lied to men but to God."*
>
> *When Ananias heard this, he fell down and died. And great*
> *fear seized all who heard what had happened. Then the young*
> *men came forward, wrapped up his body, and carried him out*
> *and buried him.*
>
> *About three hours later his wife came in, not knowing what*
> *had happened. Peter asked her, "Tell me, is this the price you*
> *and Ananias got for the land?" "Yes," she said, "that is the*
> *price." Peter said to her, "How could you agree to test the*
> *Spirit of the Lord? Look! The feet of the men who buried your*
> *husband are at the door, and they will carry you out also."*
>
> *At that moment she fell down at his feet and died. Then the*
> *young men came in and, finding her dead, carried her out and*
> *buried her beside her husband. Great fear seized the whole*
> *church and all who heard about these events. (Acts 5:1-11)*

Although we can only speculate about the respective causes of death, the link with their particularly serious sin is clear.

1 Corinthians 11 describes at length Paul's account of the institution of a sacrament (a ceremony with a specific spiritual meaning) that most sections of the Christian church celebrate regularly. It involves using bread and wine as symbols of Jesus' body and blood to remind us of him, and is variously called Holy Communion, the Eucharist, the Lord's Supper or the Breaking of Bread:

> *For I received from the Lord what I also passed on to you: The*
> *Lord Jesus, on the night he was betrayed, took bread, and when*
> *he had given thanks, he broke it and said, "This is my body,*
> *which is for you; do this in remembrance of me." In the same*
> *way, after supper he took the cup, saying, "This cup is the new*
> *covenant in my blood; do this, whenever you drink it, in*
> *remembrance of me." For whenever you eat this bread and*
> *drink this cup, you proclaim the Lord's death until he comes.*
> *(1 Corinthians 11:23-26)*

Paul goes on immediately to give a warning to the Corinthian church:

> *Therefore, whoever eats the bread or drinks the cup of the Lord*
> *in an unworthy manner will be guilty of sinning against the*
> *body and blood of the Lord. A man ought to examine himself*

> *before he eats of the bread and drinks of the cup. For anyone*
> *who eats and drinks without recognising the body of the Lord*
> *eats and drinks judgment on himself. That is why many*
> *among you are weak and sick, and a number of you have fallen*
> *asleep. (1 Corinthians 11:27-30)*

Paul means that some had died. The Corinthians' sin in abusing this solemn remembrance had directly caused disease and death.

So, what should we do about sin?

It is a good public health maxim that prevention is better than cure. As individuals we should seek to avoid sin by finding out what God's standards are and by obeying them. As a profession we should beware practices and policies that encourage our patients and colleagues to sin. As a nation we should use law wisely and well, for its teaching role as well as its policing role. It has been said that we cannot legislate to make the human heart good but we can legislate to limit the damage the human heart can do.

But we must remember at all times that there is an effective remedy for sin itself. As we will see in chapter twelve, *How should Christians pray for healing?* the question of sin, if it arises at all, can be dealt with very simply and easily by confession and claiming the forgiveness which through Christ is the right of repentant Christians. Sin cuts us off from God and therefore makes us less than whole. The route back to wholeness and holiness can be a rapid one.

But as the biblical examples in this chapter show, as we all know from our experience in everyday and professional life, sadly the physical consequences of sin may remain. That is all the more reason for taking it seriously and working against it.

10

Do demons cause disease and death?

What are demons?

The word demons is often used metaphorically in everyday life. People say, 'X has his demons' to talk about particularly striking characteristics of X that seem to be a significant cause of his behaviour. We all understand that this usage is not intended to suggest anything specifically spiritual, and the explanations for those characteristics are usually to be found back in X's personal psychosocial history.

But the Bible frequently speaks of demons (devils in older translations) or evil spirits – see the extracts below from Mark's gospel or look at the lists of healing miracles in the Appendices. The biblical picture is very clear that these demons are personal agents of evil, who have effects on the way people behave, and on their mental and physical health.

Who is the devil?

So far in this book I have said very little about the devil, though when we were earlier discussing the Fall in chapter two, *What does it mean to be human?* we saw that he was there in the Garden of Eden in the form of the serpent who tempted woman and then man into sin and spoiled it all for ever. Revelation, the last book of the Bible, consists of a particular kind of prophecy foretelling the future, which has not yet been fulfilled and therefore requires particularly careful interpretation. It identifies a great dragon in a vision with the devil: 'The great dragon was hurled down – that ancient serpent called the devil or Satan, who leads the whole world astray. He was hurled to the earth, and his angels with him' (Revelation 12:9).

The Bible throughout acknowledges Satan as a real entity, though there is more emphasis on him in the New Testament than in the Old. He is a rebel spiritual being who is allowed by God to have some spiritual power for a while. We see the devil put Jesus through a prolonged series of temptations in the desert:

> *Jesus, full of the Holy Spirit, returned from the Jordan and was led by the Spirit in the desert, where for forty days he was tempted by the devil. He ate nothing during those days, and at the end of them he was hungry. The devil said to him, "If you are the Son of God, tell this stone to become bread." Jesus answered, "It is written: 'Man does not live on bread alone.'"*
>
> *The devil led him up to a high place and showed him in an instant all the kingdoms of the world. And he said to him, "I will give you all their authority and splendour, for it has been given to me, and I can give it to anyone I want to. So if you worship me, it will all be yours." Jesus answered, "It is written: 'Worship the Lord your God and serve him only.'"*
>
> *The devil led him to Jerusalem and had him stand on the highest point of the temple. "If you are the Son of God,'" he said, "throw yourself down from here. For it is written: 'He will command his angels concerning you to guard you carefully; they will lift you up in their hands, so that you will not strike your foot against a stone.' Jesus answered, "It says: 'Do not put the Lord your God to the test.'" When the devil had finished all this tempting, he left him until an opportune time.* (Luke 4:1-13 although there is a parallel account in Matthew 4:1-11 and a summary in Mark 1:12-13)

The devil is an accuser skilled in argument with us. He sows seeds of doubt: twice he uses the expression to Jesus, 'If you are the son of God…' The devil is a liar (regarding 'all the kingdoms of the world' he could not and would not have delivered 'all their authority and splendour'). In John 8:44 Jesus says, '…there is no truth in him. When he lies, he speaks his native language, for he is a liar and the father of lies'. The devil is a tempter. The temptations Jesus faced constitute three classes that include all the temptations we face:

- physical appetites
- covetousness for more possessions
- desire for the wrong kind of spiritual power

The writer to the Hebrews later says that Jesus '…has been tempted in every way, just as we are – yet was without sin' (Hebrews 4:15). It is because of his sinless nature that his sacrifice on the cross can atone for our sins. Yet despite this awesome holiness we can talk to him in prayer about our temptations because he has been there too.

On each occasion Jesus resists the devil with a greater spiritual power. Note that on each occasion he defeats the devil because of his knowledge of the truth. Each time he replies, 'It is written...' before quoting the appropriate portion of scripture. Third time round, the devil adopts this tactic back at Jesus and quotes at length from Psalm 91:11-12. He is not an adversary to be underestimated! Jesus' commitment to the truth of scripture (and of course he only had access to what we now call the Old Testament) should inspire a similar commitment in us, whatever subject we look at – including this particularly difficult one of demons.

Having considered some of these characteristics of the devil, we should note finally that just as God has spiritual agents or messengers in the form of angels, so Satan has agents in the form of demons or evil spirits.

What does the Bible say about demons?

The Bible is quite clear that they exist and indeed regularly links deliverance from demons with healing from disease. For example the healings and deliverances of Jesus recorded in Mark's short gospel include:

> • *Just then a man in their synagogue who was possessed by an evil spirit cried out, "What do you want with us, Jesus of Nazareth? Have you come to destroy us? I know who you are – the Holy One of God!" "Be quiet!" said Jesus sternly. "Come out of him!" The evil spirit shook the man violently and came out of him with a shriek. The people were all so amazed that they asked each other, "What is this? A new teaching – and with authority! He even gives orders to evil spirits and they obey him." (Mark 1:23-27)*

> • *That evening after sunset the people brought to Jesus all the sick and demon-possessed. The whole town gathered at the door, and Jesus healed many who had various diseases. He also drove out many demons, but he would not let the demons speak because they knew who he was. (Mark 1:32-34)*

> • *So he travelled throughout Galilee, preaching in their synagogues and driving out demons. (Mark 1:39)*

> • *They went across the lake to the region of the Gerasenes. When Jesus got out of the boat, a man with an evil spirit came from the tombs to meet him. This man lived in the tombs, and no-one could bind him any more, not even with a chain. For he*

had often been chained hand and foot, but he tore the chains apart and broke the irons on his feet. No-one was strong enough to subdue him. Night and day among the tombs and in the hills he would cry out and cut himself with stones...(Mark 5:1-20)

• *...a woman whose little daughter was possessed by an evil spirit came and fell at his feet...Then he told her, "For such a reply, you may go; the demon has left your daughter." She went home and found her child lying on the bed, and the demon gone. (Mark 7:24-30)*

• *A man in the crowd answered, "Teacher, I brought you my son, who is possessed by a spirit that has robbed him of speech. Whenever it seizes him, it throws him to the ground. He foams at the mouth, gnashes his teeth and becomes rigid..." ...When the spirit saw Jesus, it immediately threw the boy into a convulsion. He fell to the ground and rolled around, foaming at the mouth. Jesus asked the boy's father, "How long has he been like this?" "From childhood," he answered. "It has often thrown him into fire or water to kill him. But if you can do anything, take pity on us and help us." "If you can?" said Jesus. "Everything is possible for him who believes." Immediately the boy's father exclaimed, "I do believe; help me overcome my unbelief!" When Jesus saw that a crowd was running to the scene, he rebuked the evil spirit. "You deaf and dumb spirit," he said, "I command you, come out of him and never enter him again." The spirit shrieked, convulsed him violently and came out. The boy looked so much like a corpse that many said, "He's dead." But Jesus took him by the hand and lifted him to his feet, and he stood up. (Mark 9:17-29)*

In these accounts we see the superior power of Jesus over these powers, whatever they may be. We read about the effect of these demonstrations on people around. We see the question of faith raised and will consider that much further in the next chapter. But we also read at least two descriptions where, as a doctor, I can see alternative medical explanations for the symptoms and signs.

The disturbed and violent man in Mark chapter five who lived among the tombs and mutilated himself sounds as if he had a psychotic illness with delusions. Yet it is reported that Jesus drove many evil spirits from him into a large herd of pigs and after this he is described as, '...the man who had been possessed by the legion of demons, sitting there, dressed and in his right mind'. He was certainly healed – but of what?

The description of the boy in Mark chapter nine sounds remarkably like a classic description of childhood-onset *grand mal* epilepsy. Why invoke evil spirits? Was Mark just recording the limited cultural explanation of the day as best as he in his ignorance could understand it? Can we with our greater neurological understanding cheerfully dispense with the concept of demons? Or, given that we know that a grand mal fit can be the final outcome of a whole range of pathologies, could it be that on that occasion a demon caused epilepsy itself or mimicked it? Does the Bible mean today exactly what it said then?

Is my problem that I am in danger of being dualistic and of not being holistic enough in my assessment? In these two examples, could the diseases – one perhaps psychiatric and the other possibly neurological – be entirely explicable in natural terms and also at the same time be caused by demons?

Should we take a literal or a metaphorical view?

The Bible is quite clear about demons (and angels) and I have already confirmed my commitment to its truthfulness, whilst accepting the need to interpret it properly. But I have also acknowledged that God has revealed himself in two books, the book of Scripture and the book of his creation, which we can learn about through observation and scientific study. Scientific study in psychology and psychiatry has come to give us apparently different explanations for behaviour.

Whichever faith we hold (indeed, even if we don't have hold any), none of us would deny that there is evil in the world. We are all ethical beings; as we saw in chapter two, that is part of what being made in the image of God means. If we are honest, we all acknowledge the daily reality of wrong choices with bad consequences. (In chapter nine I suggested that the difference between believer and non-believer is not about the reality of sin but about the significance of that sin.) Evil is one word for describing situations at the extreme end of the spectrum of wrong-choices-with-bad-consequences. We all accept the reality of evil.

Further, most of us would recognise the reality of corporate or institutional evil. Obvious examples are the culture that led to the atrocities of the Nazis or some manifestations of Communist totalitarianism. There is an ever-growing protest movement around the world about the perceived evils of global capitalism. Certainly, the grossly unfair distribution of resources between the rich world and the poor world is an evil with major effects on health.

Whilst there might be more reservations about what degree of behaviour constitutes personal evil, some people for example confining that description to the rare mass murderer, I similarly do not think there is much doubt about the reality of personal evil. Should we perhaps search our hearts sometimes to see whether our own actions ever constitute personal evil? Reflecting on the nature of temptation, sometimes we all give in because we like to indulge this appetite so much that we cannot resist it on occasion. These are our experiences of evil. Both corporate and personal, evil is real.

But is evil always to be explained in modern Western sociological or psychological terms by the effects of poor upbringing and unfortunate life events, or of the chance occurrence of adverse circumstances? Is there ever a personal source of evil, caused by the biblical devil, at work in a more direct and more tangible way?

Professor Andrew Sims, one time President of the Royal College of Psychiatrists, has written very helpfully on the question of demons within psychiatric practice, as has Professor Chris Cook (see *References and Further Reading* at the end of the chapter). Partly because of a growing personal commitment to the literal truth of scripture – the older I get, the more I realise that the Bible means exactly what it says – and partly because of a few clinical experiences (one of which is described below), I have come to take a more literal view. I believe that ascriptions of physical or psychological problems to the demonic usually have explanations which are entirely natural, and we must beware the thinking that absolves the individual from personal responsibility: 'My demons made me do it'. But on rare occasions I believe the explanation is supernatural, demonic and occult. The word occult actually means hidden – as in the testing of stool specimens for faecal occult bloods – and therefore we would not expect such explanations necessarily to be immediately apparent. I believe that the demonic, though rare, exists.

For me, C S Lewis put the overall position best back in 1941 in his classic *The Screwtape Letters*, a delightful book based on a postulated correspondence between a senior and a junior devil, which uses humour to make a lot of powerful points about the nature of temptation. In the preface Lewis wrote: 'There are two equal and opposite errors into which our race can fall about the devils. One is to disbelieve in their existence. The other is to believe, and to feel an excessive and unhealthy interest in them. They themselves are equally pleased by both errors and hail a materialist or a magician with the same delight.'

Real but rare?

I believe Lewis' position squares both with the Bible and my (limited) experience. In clinical practice in the UK, I believe the hard end of the occult is real but rare. In ten years' general practice, with about 10,000 face-to-face consultations a year, I made a provisional diagnosis of the frankly occult on only half a dozen occasions. An incidence of five to six per 100,000 is not that common – but then there are rarer medical conditions GPs are supposed to be able to recognise and treat. So we should be open to the possibility.

When I met patients with symptoms that did not seem to fit any medically recognisable pattern, I would extend my history taking to spiritual areas. I would ask gentle open questions about involvement in occult practices. A clear 'No' to everything from horoscopes through Tarot cards to séances usually meant that I could dismiss the subject. Any positive response required further investigation. People who have invested much of themselves in supernatural activities are more likely to have problems in that area, which can only be alleviated by a spiritual approach.

What is deliverance ministry?

Deliverance ministry is the name given to the range of spiritual approaches seeking to help those who have problems associated with the demonic. It is clearly controversial and can be dangerous if the diagnosis is wrong, or if the 'treatment' is applied wrongly even with a right diagnosis. In Britain there was a major enquiry into the tragic death of a young girl called Victoria Climbié who died in 1999 after neglect and abuse by members of her family. During the enquiry it became clear that a local charismatic church had been performing deliverance ministry on her, believing mistakenly but in all sincerity that she was demonised. Had a more accurate diagnosis been made, and many other (professional) agencies who were better equipped to make the diagnosis were involved as well, the outcome might have been different.

If I am right and the demonic is real but rare, then explanations like psychiatric conditions, physical disease and abuse must first be excluded. Once the likely diagnosis has been confirmed, the prayer ministry, which is essentially no different in principle from that of routine Christian prayer for healing, needs to be done in an appropriate way. In 1974 an exorcism was linked with a tragic death. (Incidentally, the Bible uses – in some versions – the word exorcist to refer only to the charlatans described in Acts 19:13, so that the expression the *ministry of deliverance* is probably more appropriate than exorcism.) As a consequence of this death, in 1975 Dr Donald Coggan, the then Archbishop of Canterbury, issued guidelines for good practice on behalf of the Church of England House of Bishops. Deliverance ministry should be performed:

- in collaboration with the resources of medicine
- in the context of prayer and sacrament
- with the minimum of publicity
- by experienced persons authorised by the diocesan bishop
- with follow up by continued pastoral care

I suggest that other denominations should apply these principles within their own ways of worshipping. I have no experience of such in my own church but I once prayed in general practice for a patient with a problem I thought might be supernatural in origin, with interesting results. I recount the story, as it certainly illustrates the importance of taking a whole person approach and that spiritual treatments may occasionally be appropriate and effective.

The patient was a woman of late middle age, with a very thick bundle of case notes. It has been said that the prognosis of the patient is inversely proportional to the thickness of the notes, and in her case that was probably true. She had chronic tension headaches: due to anxiety, her neck muscles tensed up and caused headache at the back of her head. This frightened her and made her worry about all sorts of serious diagnoses such as having a brain tumour. This made her more anxious, so her neck muscles tensed up further, making her headache even worse. It was an example of the proverbial vicious circle. She had been extensively investigated and all the high technology tests were negative. Psychiatrists had not helped. My simple reassurance and prescriptions of moderate painkillers and muscle relaxants hadn't done much either.

One morning I arrived at the practice to discover that she had required a home visit from the emergency doctor in the night. Around mid-morning I followed that up and listened to her story. Apparently, the day before she had decided to attend a spiritual healer for help with her headaches. One of the local churches had unwisely opened its doors to a spiritual healer, who was not offering Christian prayer for healing but was channelling spiritual forces through a particular power that he claimed to have. He had placed his hands on her head and for a short period performed whatever healing he practised.

Unfortunately, her headache not only failed to improve but became very much worse. For that reason she had phoned for an emergency home visit in the night and had been given a powerful analgesic injection. By mid-morning, she was in severe pain again. There was nothing new on physical examination but the striking finding was the most extreme degree of fear that I had ever seen her in.

I explained to her and to her husband who was in the same room that I thought there might be a spiritual diagnosis here, and I asked if I might pray a simple prayer for her, there and then. They both agreed readily. I sat across the room from her, some ten feet away, and prayed out loud a very short and simple prayer that God would touch her, take away her pain, and remove any harmful effects of any kind that might have followed the incident with the spiritual healer the day before. Immediately, two things happened.

The first was, and remains, entirely objective. Her fear, tension and pain disappeared immediately and she sat up with a smile on her face. The second was subjective and I will never know if I imagined it or not: I had an overpowering sensation of something extremely cold crossing the floor and leaving the room. I shivered violently.

So, what was the explanation for her improvement? Was it all at a psychological level, that my simple words were no more than a trigger for an abreaction for her? At some psychological level, had she flicked a mental switch and cut off the neural impulses causing the muscle tension, abolishing her headache immediately?

Or was it at a spiritual level? 'Talk therapy' had never done anything for her before. By any account, her improvement was certainly a significant and wonderful answer to prayer for healing, and fell into the second dictionary category described in chapters five and seven. But was it more than a thrilling example of an answer to prayer for healing? Indeed, had there been some prior demonic involvement, some spiritual oppression resulting from her contact with the non-Christian healer? Had I (however unwittingly) performed deliverance ministry?

It would be a great story if she never had headaches again. Sadly, she was back in the consulting room within a week or so, with the same mixture as before. I never prayed with her again and I don't recall that whole episode doing anything else for her or her husband spiritually. She was glad to be better for a while, but to my knowledge it didn't give her any interest at all in Christian things.

I do not think this anecdote has much objective force in argument but it makes a number of points relating to different discussions in this book. I will refer to it again in chapter twelve, *How should Christians pray for healing?*

Do demons cause death?

This chapter so far has only considered the question, 'Do demons cause disease?' What about, 'Do demons cause death?' I have only talked about UK practice. We hear stories from areas of the developing world where Satan is sometimes worshipped more openly (and therefore perhaps could have more power) where death has been reported to follow occult activities. Although I have no first hand knowledge of such events, I am open to this possibility. It is another reason why we should avoid an excessive and unhealthy interest and never go looking for the devil, but be ready for him when, rarely, he appears.

Writing to the Christians at Ephesus, towards the end of his letter, Paul gives a clear reminder that the real struggles of the Christian life are not about human issues but reflect a spiritual battle:

> *Finally, be strong in the Lord and in his mighty power. Put on the full armour of God so that you can take your stand against the devil's schemes. For our struggle is not against flesh and blood, but against the rulers, against the authorities, against the powers of this dark world and against the spiritual forces of evil in the heavenly realms. (Ephesians 6:10-12)*

We have a real adversary we should take seriously. Christians may disagree about whether the devil is only a symbol for evil worked through the temptations to which we are all prone in a fallen world, or whether he and his demons are real and should be considered in a literal way. But we should not make the error of disbelieving in his existence. He is a significant factor in healthcare.

References and Further Reading

A Time to Heal. London: Church House Publishing, 2000
ISBN 0 7151 3837 5
Chapter 9, *Deliverance from Evil* is balanced and helpful; it gives the reference to the House of Bishops guidelines as: General Synod, *Report of Proceedings*, Volume 6, No 2, July 1975

Cook C. Demon Possession and Mental Illness. *Nucleus* 1997; July:13-17
This is the undergraduate journal of the Christian Medical Fellowship and can be viewed on the CMF website www.cmf.org.uk

Lewis CS. *The Screwtape Letters.* London: Collins, 1979
ISBN 0 00 216732 8

Sims ACP. *Demon Possession: Medical Perspective in a Western Culture* in *Medicine and the Bible.* Exeter: CMF/Paternoster Press, 1986
ISBN 0 85364 423 3

Must you have faith to be healed?

What is faith?

The Bible states, 'Now faith is being sure of what we hope for and certain of what we do not see' (Hebrews 11:1). The quotation in this chapter's title linking faith and healing comes from a short account in Acts:

> *In Lystra there sat a man crippled in his feet, who was lame from birth and had never walked. He listened to Paul as he was speaking. Paul looked directly at him, saw that he had faith to be healed and called out, "Stand up on your feet!" At that, the man jumped up and began to walk. (Acts 14:8-10)*

This man's faith seems to have been central to Paul taking the decision to give a command to be healed, and that command seems to have activated whatever power was necessary for the healing. So, is faith always required for supernatural healing? In the New Testament's accounts of healing (see chapter five, *What does the Bible say?* and the *Appendices*), faith in God's power to heal is always implicit and often explicit.

Does the individual seeking healing need faith?

In their gospels, Matthew, Mark and Luke all narrate a double account of Jesus raising from the dead a twelve year old girl and of him being interrupted on the way there by a woman with a twelve year history of menorrhagia (excessive bleeding from the womb). Mark's account of this woman's case probably holds the most interest for medical readers:

> *And a woman was there who had been subject to bleeding for twelve years. She had suffered a great deal under the care of many doctors and had spent all she had, yet instead of getting better she grew worse. When she heard about Jesus, she came up behind him in the crowd and touched his cloak, because*

> *she thought, "If I just touch his clothes, I will be healed."*
> *Immediately her bleeding stopped, and she felt in her body that*
> *she was freed from her suffering.*
>
> *At once Jesus realised that power had gone out from him. He*
> *turned around in the crowd and asked, "Who touched my*
> *clothes?" "You see the people crowding against you," his*
> *disciples answered, "and yet you can ask, 'Who touched me?'"*
> *But Jesus kept looking around to see who had done it. Then the*
> *woman, knowing what had happened to her, came and fell at*
> *his feet and, trembling with fear, told him the whole truth.*
> *He said to her, "Daughter, your faith has healed you. Go in*
> *peace and be freed from your suffering." (Mark 5:25-34. See*
> *also Matthew 9:20-22 and Luke 8:43-48)*

Her menorrhagia made her ritually unclean. She would have defiled anybody she touched while she was bleeding, and so had been cut off from family, friends and synagogue for much of the previous twelve years. Mark baldly describes the failure of the doctors of the day and, commenting on their fees, possibly hints that she was bled twice! She had incredible faith, believing that she just had to touch the clothes of Christ to be healed. This is not magic or superstition but faith: she was indeed sure of what she hoped for and certain of what she did not see.

She was healed. Her bleeding stopped and she was '...freed from her suffering'. This expression implies liberation psychologically, socially and spiritually as well as physically. She was truly made whole. In Luke 8:48 Jesus is recorded as saying to her: 'Go in peace'. She went in a state of *shalom*!

It is interesting that her faith triggered the release of healing power from Christ without him being asked or, apparently, knowing at first that it was happening. She realised that because of her touch she was guilty of having defiled Christ himself and others in the crowd, and this explains her fear at being found out. But she told the whole truth and rather than condemnation she received a commendation for her faith. The faith of this individual was certainly instrumental in her healing.

Can others have faith instead?

Faith is always involved somehow in supernatural healing, but interestingly, it is not always the faith of the person in need that is recorded. In the account we were just considering, the father of the twelve year old girl was the one with faith. It was implicit in his request to Jesus:

> *...one of the synagogue rulers, named Jairus, came there.*

> *Seeing Jesus, he fell at his feet and pleaded earnestly with him,*
> *"My little daughter is dying. Please come and put your hands*
> *on her so that she will be healed and live." So Jesus went with*
> *him. (Mark 5:22-24)*

The girl was dead when Jesus arrived – though not when he left – so any faith of hers could not be relevant at the time of the healing. It was her father's faith that was critical.

In another example, a Roman centurion came to Jesus about his sick servant:

> *When Jesus had entered Capernaum, a centurion came to him,*
> *asking for help. "Lord," he said, "my servant lies at home*
> *paralysed and in terrible suffering." Jesus said to him, "I will*
> *go and heal him." The centurion replied, "Lord, I do not*
> *deserve to have you come under my roof. But just say the word,*
> *and my servant will be healed. For I myself am a man under*
> *authority, with soldiers under me. I tell this one, 'Go,' and he*
> *goes; and that one, 'Come,' and he comes. I say to my servant,*
> *'Do this,' and he does it."*
>
> *When Jesus heard this, he was astonished and said to those*
> *following him, "I tell you the truth, I have not found anyone*
> *in Israel with such great faith..." Then Jesus said to the*
> *centurion, "Go! It will be done just as you believed it would."*
> *And his servant was healed at that very hour. (Matthew 8:5-*
> *10, 13. See also Luke 7:2-10)*

The centurion had the respect of local Jews. Luke's account tells us, '...they pleaded earnestly with him, "This man deserves to have you do this, because he loves our nation and has built our synagogue" ' (Luke 7:4-5). The centurion understood authority. He lived by giving orders and obeying those of his superiors. He recognised that Jesus had the power to heal his servant, whom he obviously cared for. Jesus contrasted this recognition with the situation among the people of Israel and called it '...such great faith'. In combination with the power of God this faith was effective in bringing about an instantaneous healing at a distance.

These two are examples of the faith of an individual on behalf of another individual. There is another case recorded in the gospels of Matthew, Mark and Luke, which illustrates group faith on behalf of an individual:

> *One day as he was teaching, Pharisees and teachers of the*
> *law, who had come from every village of Galilee and from Judea*

and Jerusalem, were sitting there. And the power of the Lord was present for him to heal the sick. Some men came carrying a paralytic on a mat and tried to take him into the house to lay him before Jesus. When they could not find a way to do this because of the crowd, they went up on the roof and lowered him on his mat through the tiles into the middle of the crowd, right in front of Jesus.

When Jesus saw their faith, he said, "Friend, your sins are forgiven." The Pharisees and the teachers of the law began thinking to themselves, "Who is this fellow who speaks blasphemy? Who can forgive sins but God alone?" Jesus knew what they were thinking and asked, "Why are you thinking these things in your hearts? Which is easier: to say, 'Your sins are forgiven,' or to say, 'Get up and walk'? But that you may know that the Son of Man has authority on earth to forgive sins..."

He said to the paralysed man, "I tell you, get up, take your mat and go home." Immediately he stood up in front of them, took what he had been lying on and went home praising God. Everyone was amazed and gave praise to God. They were filled with awe and said, "We have seen remarkable things today." (Luke 5:17-26. See also Matthew 9:2-8 and Mark 2:3-12)

This healing narrative is complicated because Jesus controversially forgave the man's sin by his authority as 'the Son of Man'; so, the healing was a demonstration of this authority. It was also a compassionate response to need, and – hence the choice for this section – a demonstration of the effect of the faith of the group of friends. Note that the healing process began '...when Jesus saw their faith...'

The man was not just cured of his paralysis but, whether any sin on his part was involved in his sickness or not, he was spiritually renewed: '...went home praising God'. He was not just cured but healed. All this discussion and the demonstration of healing had a powerful effect on those present.

These examples all show that people with faith can effectively bring others to Jesus for healing.

Does lack of faith have an effect?

Matthew 13:53-58, Mark 6:1-6 and Luke 4:16-30 all describe how Jesus was rejected in his home town of Nazareth, perhaps because familiarity breeds contempt. Both Matthew and Mark spell out that the

Nazarenes' lack of faith limited Jesus' ability to work miracles and Mark specifically discusses healing:

> *He could not do any miracles there, except lay his hands on a few sick people and heal them. And he was amazed at their lack of faith. (Mark 6:5-6)*

This example shows how in that situation there was a general inability for Jesus to heal because of lack of faith. There may be indirect evidence from another specific case. If we return to the raising from the dead of Jairus' daughter, we read specifically that Jesus limited the number of people present:

> *When Jesus entered the ruler's house and saw the flute players and the noisy crowd, he said, "Go away. The girl is not dead but asleep." But they laughed at him. After the crowd had been put outside, he went in and took the girl by the hand, and she got up. News of this spread through all that region. (Matthew 9:23-26)*

> *He did not let anyone follow him except Peter, James and John the brother of James. When they came to the home of the synagogue ruler, Jesus saw a commotion, with people crying and wailing loudly. He went in and said to them, "Why all this commotion and wailing? The child is not dead but asleep." But they laughed at him. After he put them all out, he took the child's father and mother and the disciples who were with him, and went in where the child was. (Mark 5:37-40)*

Health professionals can probably think of all sorts of reasons for limiting the numbers present: respect for privacy and dignity, concern for confidentiality, the outside chance of infection, and a need for space to think in peace are all possibilities which come readily to mind. In addition, some Christians over the years have suggested that Jesus deliberately got rid of those who lacked faith to believe that he could do this particular miracle of healing. If they had been present their lack of faith might somehow have limited his power.

So must faith be present before healing?

So, do all these examples mean there has to be faith before healing can occur? Must we have faith to be healed? Healing, whether natural or supernatural, is a work of God. He is either working within or outside the laws of his creation. Healing in the natural sense may well have involved medical intervention. Even then, we need to remember that the best endeavours of high-technology medicine all depend on the body's own inbuilt healing mechanisms. Ambroîse Paré (1510-

1590), quoted in chapter four, *What is healing?* said in Old French: *'Je le pensyt, Dieu le guaryt'* – 'I dressed it [the wound] God healed him'. That mutual contribution always remains the case today.

Supernatural healing involves God's compassion and power – though there is more to it than that – and human faith is involved somewhere, whether we can see it or not. The pattern set out in James 5:13-16 for sick people to call in the elders of the church for anointing and prayer (which we will work through thoroughly in the next chapter) is set in the context of faith and prayer.

Can there be faith without healing?
But if there must always be faith in association with healing, then we must also be real to peoples' experience and acknowledge that there can be faith without healing. Or, returning to the distinction made in chapter four between cure and healing, there are certainly many examples of faith without cure. These situations are always difficult for the people involved and we will consider them in the next chapter, *How should Christians pray for healing?* and in chapter 13, *Why does God allow suffering?*

Can there be healing without faith?
Further, experience also teaches that there can be healing without apparent faith on the part of the one healed. Jesus' miracles regularly elicited faith on the part of the one healed; in chapter five, it is cited as one of their defining characteristics. Yet contemporary experience of successful prayer for healing for those who are not Christians does not usually include the people who have been healed coming to faith.

In the last chapter I recounted at length the story of my prayer for the healing of a woman with severe headache after she visited a spiritualist healer. I thought her temporary cure was a dramatic answer to prayer, but have to admit that it never had any apparent spiritual effect on her or her husband who had witnessed it. Other Christian doctors with better tales of the unexpected after prayer for healing have given similar reports.

The late John Wimber linked what he called *power healing* with *power evangelism* and cited the example of healings reported from the developing world as effective aids to communicating the gospel of Christ. This has not been my experience in Britain and I do not believe there is evidence for it being a common phenomenon in the West.

Is there a faith formula?
It is very important that we do not confuse faith – '...being sure of what we hope for and certain of what we do not see' (Hebrews 11:1)

– with superstitions and magic. These may just be human rituals operating at psychological and social levels but some of them may cross over into the world of harmful spiritual powers and the occult. Faith is about trusting an all-powerful God.

In chapter seven, *What are Christians doing today?* I criticised the wrong theology that leads some sections of the church to conclude that, when an individual is not cured after prayer, then somebody's faith is deficient somewhere. This may be true but it is usually not the answer. There is most certainly no faith formula, no magic form of words that will always do the trick. God is not a slot machine. It is not a case of getting all the right factors lined up and then pulling the handle. We need to approach a great God with a lot more humility than that.

What else is important in prayer?

Prayer for healing is in essence no different from any other kind of prayer. So this is a convenient point to look at some of the principles involved in prayer being answered:

- **'offered in faith'**
  And the prayer offered in faith will make the sick person well; the Lord will raise him up. (James 5:15)

  This whole chapter is about faith. It is an essential part of all prayer. And would any sane person invest large amounts of their time in prayer unless they believed something was going to happen?

- **'faith as small as a mustard seed'**
  I tell you the truth, if you have faith as small as a mustard seed, you can say to this mountain, "Move from here to there" and it will move. Nothing will be impossible for you. (Matthew 17:20)

  The dialogue that ends with this astonishing statement follows the disciples asking why they could not heal the boy with epilepsy and a demon. The disciples ask, 'Why couldn't we drive it out?' and Jesus replies, 'Because you have so little faith', before talking about the tiny amount (in his eyes) of faith needed to move mountains.

- **'if you have faith and do not doubt'**
  Jesus replied, "I tell you the truth, if you have faith and do not doubt, not only can you do what was done to the fig-tree, but also you can say to this mountain, 'Go, throw yourself into the sea,' and it will be

done. If you believe, you will receive whatever you ask for in prayer."
(Matthew 21:21-22)

A fig-tree had just withered at Jesus' command and the disciples were amazed. He responded with this further teaching about faith moving mountains, and ended with the challenging statement that begins, 'If you believe...'

- **'if two of you on earth agree'**
Again, I tell you that if two of you on earth agree about anything you ask for, it will be done for you by my Father in heaven. For where two or three come together in my name, there am I with them. (Matthew 18:19-20)

There is strength in numbers. God cares about community. From these verses we can conclude that he is the more willing to be present with groups of people (even if the number is just two) who meet for his purposes, and to respond to what they ask.

- **'whatever you ask in my name'**
And I will do whatever you ask in my name, so that the Son may bring glory to the Father. You may ask me for anything in my name, and I will do it. (John 14:13-14)

The expression 'in my name' hints at far more than a formulaic use of the word Jesus. It is about being centred on God and being anxious for glory to be given to him. Even though many Christians end all their prayers '...in Jesus' name, Amen', these words in themselves are not magic and cannot in themselves achieve anything unless the underlying approach is correct.

- **'according to his will'**
This is the assurance we have in approaching God: that if we ask anything according to his will, he hears us. And if we know that he hears us – whatever we ask – we know that we have what we asked of him. (1 John 5:14-15)

The concept 'according to his will' does start to introduce an explanation for why prayers are not always answered as we would want them to be.

God always answers prayer, but the way he answers has been compared to traffic lights. Sometimes he gives the green light: 'Go!' Straight away we get what we asked. Other times there is the amber light: 'Wait!' We need patience and persistence in prayer as we wait. Most of us find this very hard. Sometimes God's answer is the red light: 'No!' What we have asked has not been in accordance with his will; he has something better for us. All good parents have to say 'No!' to their children sometimes and Christians are the children of God.

- **'everyone who asks receives'**
  Ask and it will be given to you; seek and you will find; knock and the door will be opened to you. For everyone who asks receives; he who seeks finds; and to him who knocks the door will be opened. (Luke 11:9-10)

The whole tenor of the Bible regarding prayer is one of, in the modern idiom, 'Go for it!' It is a favourite sermon aid for preachers to point out that the first letters of 'Ask... seek... knock...' make up the acrostic ask.

John Wimber is possibly best remembered for his saying: 'Faith is spelled r-i-s-k'. Like most doctors, I am an innately cautious person but all my Christian understanding and experience encourage me that we should 'Go for it!' in prayer. How we do that sensibly and safely is the subject of the next chapter.

Should we use the expression faith healing?

We have a problem with language in what we are going to move on to in the next chapter, namely praying for healing. Faith healing is now an unhelpful term. It suggests that the power is not in a gracious God but in the faith itself, and raises the question of some sort of faith formula: if you just get the words or the process right then healing will automatically follow. This is not the case.

Spiritual healing says nothing of the source of the power. Members of the National Federation of Spiritual Healers (which is active, at least by advertising, in many hospitals) may be tapping into a power not of God, as I believe the anecdote about my patient in chapter ten illustrates.

The single word healing means all things to all men and would generally be considered nowadays under the umbrella of complementary/alternative medicine. It is therefore best avoided.

I believe the correct expression for what we come to consider now is Christian prayer for healing.

References and Further Reading

Wimber J with Springer K. *Power Healing*. London: Hodder and Stoughton, 1986
ISBN 0 340 39090 5
Wimber links healing with power evangelism on pages 60-61.

12

How should Christians pray for healing?

Should Christians pray for healing?

This prior question is important. If God does not heal today in answer to prayer, or if for some convincing reason it could be demonstrated from the Bible that Christians should not pray for healing, then the question 'How?' is not relevant. But I argued in chapter five that the commissioning of the disciples to preach and heal, the Great Commission of Matthew 28:18-20 to all the church for the rest of time, the specific if more controversial commission of Mark 16:18, and the general injunction of James 5:13-16 all suggest that prayer for healing should still be carried out today.

In the last chapter I argued that the whole tenor of the Bible with regard to prayer is one of 'Go for it!' I can see no reason why prayer for healing should be in any different category. Whilst some Christians may disagree, it is clear that we should pray for healing. The rest of this chapter will therefore concentrate on how.

Does the Bible give us principles?

In chapter five we noted that in his letter James gives very specific teaching:

> Is any one of you in trouble? He should pray. Is anyone happy? Let him sing songs of praise. Is any one of you sick? He should call the elders of the church to pray over him and anoint him with oil in the name of the Lord. And the prayer offered in faith will make the sick person well; the Lord will raise him up. If he has sinned, he will be forgiven. Therefore confess your sins to each other and pray for each other so that you may be healed. The prayer of a righteous man is powerful and effective. (James 5:13-16)

I believe this sets a pattern for normative church practice for all time. Let us work through this passage in detail, looking for principles and exploring how they might work in practice in the 21st century. Christian healing:

- **is available for all**
  The words any one are emphasised three times at the beginning of this important passage: 'Is any one of you in trouble? He should pray. Is anyone happy? Let him sing songs of praise. Is any one of you sick?' Christian prayer for healing can be offered to anyone. It is available for all.

- **should be patient centred**
  It is the responsibility of the one who is sick to '...call the elders of the church'. This does not mean it is necessarily wrong for responsible Christians to raise the subject of prayer for healing with somebody. Whoever initiates it, the whole process should remain respectfully centred on the patient. I have had the privilege of working with the UK General Medical Council in regulating how doctors relate to their patients, and for me there are strong parallels between this aspect of medical regulation and the proper approach to Christian healing.

- **should be practised responsibly**
  The emphasis on the elders of the church indicates that prayer for healing should not be carried out trivially or in an irresponsible way. Elders in the Bible (also called overseers or bishops and different denominations perfectly reasonably interpret this teaching differently) are the leaders of churches and a very high standard is expected of them:

> *An elder must be blameless, the husband of but one wife, a man whose children believe and are not open to the charge of being wild and disobedient. Since an overseer is entrusted with God's work, he must be blameless – not overbearing, not quick-tempered, not given to much wine, not violent, not pursuing dishonest gain. Rather he must be hospitable, one who loves what is good, who is self-controlled, upright, holy and disciplined. He must hold firmly to the trustworthy message as it has been taught, so that he can encourage others by sound doctrine and refute those who oppose it. (Titus 1:6-9. See also 1 Timothy 3:2-7)*

This daunting person specification requires elders to be mature, trained, experienced and accountable people. It is tempting again to draw comparisons with the training and accountability of health professionals. While it does not mean that anyone is barred from praying for healing or that only the experienced should be involved (that would be against the 'Go for it!' tenor of the Bible's approach to prayer), it does confirm that prayer for healing should always be undertaken responsibly.

There is no specific suggestion in James that the elders should have gifts of healing (1 Corinthians 12:9, 28). We considered in chapter seven whether these refer to natural or supernatural gifts. I have come across at least one individual whom I would describe as having a supernatural gift in this area. Along with those who are far more experienced in this field than I am, I believe that the part supernatural gifting has to play in Christian prayer for healing is small.

It has been suggested that 'He should call the elders of the church...' establishes a pattern for more serious sickness. The individual is too unwell to attend church where perhaps prayer for healing is routine, so needs a home visit. 'The elders' (plural) constitutes the quorum for effective prayer mentioned in the previous chapter: 'For where two or three come together in my name, there am I with them' (Matthew 18:20). From a practical point of view their mutual insights may be complementary and their joint presence may further reassure the patient as well as providing checks and balances.

- **involves prayer**

'He should call the elders of the church to pray over him.' Prayer is a means of communication with God. It does not just involve asking for things. Jesus gave the church a model for prayer in what we usually call the Lord's Prayer. Note that his introduction of it in Matthew 6:9 begins, 'This is how you should pray...' not, 'This is what you should pray'. There is no particular formula, no special set of words. The Lord's Prayer turns our focus onto God, makes us acknowledge our shortcomings, encourages us to seek God's protection from temptation, and keeps requests to a minimum.

Our prayers can be brief: 'And when you pray, do not keep on babbling like pagans, for they think they will be heard because of their many words. Do not be like them, for your Father knows what you need before you ask him' (Matthew 6:7-8).

There really is no special way of praying. We come in humility to a great God. We come like children to a parent.

- **may involve symbols**

'...to pray over him and anoint him with oil in the name of the Lord.' Anointing with oil will be considered in some detail below, but it is one of several symbolic aspects that some

Christians choose to involve alongside prayer for healing. Others are the laying on of hands and, arguably, an association with the sacrament of Holy Communion.

- **is associated with faith**

We considered this at length in the previous chapter. James tells us categorically here that '...the prayer offered in faith will make the sick person well; the Lord will raise him up'. All true prayer involves faith, but the importance of this faith – whether it be that of the one prayed for, the elders or both parties – is emphasised here. The word *sozo* we considered in chapter four is used here for 'make the sick person well'. The likeliest meaning of 'the Lord will raise him up' is the literal one that he will get up from his sickbed.

- **is associated with forgiveness of sin**

'If he has sinned, he will be forgiven.' We considered the links between sin, sickness and death extensively in chapter nine. There is no suggestion of course here in James that the sick person had never sinned, nor that the sickness was necessarily due to sin. Those of us who have suffered serious illness know that sickness often gives us time to think; the patient may have recalled unconfessed sin that needed to be dealt with alongside physical recovery.

'Therefore confess your sins to each other and pray for each other so that you may be healed.' This is probably a general exhortation in a community context, to remind us of the need for forgiveness of sin and consequent wholeness and health in the Christian community.

Although these seven principles complete the list of lessons about Christian healing that can be drawn from this passage in James, we should note that he goes on to say, 'The prayer of a righteous man is powerful and effective'. He does not miss the opportunity to make these general points about prayer and about those who pray. He goes on to illustrate their importance from the example of Elijah the miracle worker, with the surprising but encouraging announcement, 'Elijah was a man just like us' (James 5:17).

This reminds us that if we are going to pray for healing we must be righteous. This means that we must be living right lives all the time, confessing our sins and finding forgiveness as soon as we become aware of them. Probably we should prepare ourselves by specific confession for each occasion of prayer for healing.

How should we pray for healing in the church context?

The practical outworking of the principles outlined above will depend on the denomination in question. Many churches hold regular services designated as Healing Services or, perhaps more appropriately, Services of Prayer for Healing. The charismatic and Pentecostal churches are likely to pray for healing in the context of their exuberant worship style, while most Anglican and other mainstream denominational churches are likely to have a special service, with a specific liturgy.

In cases of need occurring between such services and where the patient is too sick to attend church, leaders and others from church may attend the patient at home, exactly as described in James.

Particular questions that may be raised in some traditions include:

- Should prayer for healing take place during Holy Communion?
- Should the person being prayed for be anointed with oil?
- Should prayer for healing involve the laying on of hands?

Should prayer for healing accompany Holy Communion?

In chapter five, *What does the Bible say?* we considered the question, 'Is there healing in the atonement?' On the theological principles, we concluded both 'Yes' and 'No'. Whatever conclusions different Christians may come to on this theoretical question, it is nevertheless common for services of prayer for healing to be associated with services for Holy Communion. Given that healing is about wholeness and that this sense of wholeness (of atonement: at-one-ment with God and at-one-ment with fellow Christians) is probably greatest immediately after Communion, it seems a most appropriate time to pray for healing. But prayer for healing can certainly take place apart from Communion.

What about anointing with oil?

Anointing with oil is mentioned in connection with healing in Mark's gospel: 'They went out and preached that people should repent. They drove out many demons and anointed many sick people with oil and healed them' (Mark 6:12-13). There are three main understandings of this and the injunction in James about anointing with oil in the context of prayer for healing today. Anointing has been thought to be:

- **sacramental**

  A sacrament is an outward sign of an inner blessing. Different sections of the church recognise different numbers of sacraments. My own church only recognises two, the Lord's Supper and believer's baptism. The Roman Catholic Church also recognises other sacraments including the Sacrament of the Sick, where the priest anoints the sick person with specially consecrated oil. The underlying belief is that the oil is an effective medium of forgiveness for those no longer able to make conscious confession of sin.

  It is interesting to note that the Catholic church has only relatively recently returned to this understanding. There is a prayer in *Alcuin's Rite of Anointing* (circa 735-804): 'Through the anointing of consecrated oil and our prayers, cured and warmed by the Holy Spirit, may you merit to receive your former health and even better health.' However, the purpose of anointing later came to be seen as a preparation for death. In the twelfth century, Peter Lombard (circa 1100-1160) wrote: 'Unction prepares those who are departing this world for the divine vision'. Anointing became known as 'Extreme Unction'. The Roman Catholic Church has recently returned to viewing anointing as a sacrament for healing.

- **pharmaceutical**

  There are both Old and New Testament examples of oil as a therapeutic agent:

  > From the sole of your foot to the top of your head there is no soundness – only wounds and welts and open sores, not cleansed or bandaged or soothed with oil. (Isaiah 1:6)

  > But a Samaritan, as he travelled, came where the man was; and when he saw him, he took pity on him. He went to him and bandaged his wounds, pouring on oil and wine. (Luke 10:33-34)

  Although oil was understood at the time to have therapeutic properties, this is unlikely to be the reason why James mentions it. Oil was not believed to be effective for all conditions but James gives a general injunction applying to all sick people.

- **ceremonial**

  In the Bible, oil is a sign of commissioning:

  > Then Samuel took a flask of oil and poured it on Saul's head and kissed him, saying, "Has not the Lord anointed you leader over his inheritance?" (1 Samuel 10:1)

> *So Samuel took the horn of oil and anointed him in the presence*
> *of his brothers, and from that day on the Spirit of the Lord came*
> *upon David in power. (1 Samuel 16:13)*

Today, before a British monarch is crowned, the Archbishop of Canterbury similarly anoints them to prepare him/her for office. Anointing is also a sign of honour and Luke 7:36-50 describes 'a woman who had lived a sinful life' who anoints Jesus' feet with perfume, sparking off a theological discussion between Jesus and Simon the Pharisee. Oil is a sign of joy: Isaiah 61:3 talks about 'the oil of gladness instead of mourning'. The psalmist combines the concepts of honour and joy in the best known of all the Psalms: 'You prepare a table before me in the presence of my enemies. You anoint my head with oil; my cup overflows' (Psalm 23:5).

Finally, the words *Christ* (Greek) and *Messiah* (Hebrew) both mean 'the Anointed One.' When we call ourselves Christians we are emphasising our oneness with our Lord as anointed ones. Oil is thus a very appropriate symbol within the Christian healing ministry, and most would regard its use as symbolic and ceremonial.

What about the laying on of hands?

Like the use of anointing, the laying on of hands is not directly therapeutic in itself but is symbolic. It is about comforting and supporting the one prayed for, and about identifying with them. Touching the distressed is a very natural human thing to do. It is sometimes recorded that Jesus touched people when he healed them.

> *When the sun was setting, the people brought to Jesus all who*
> *had various kinds of sickness, and laying his hands on each*
> *one, he healed them. (Luke 4:40)*

In chapter five, *What does the Bible say?* we considered the controversy about the longer ending to Mark's gospel, and concluded we should be cautious about deriving church practice from it. Yet in Mark 16:17-18 we read, '…those who believe…will place their hands on sick people, and they will get well'.

If in the church context we are to lay hands on people as we pray for them, and I have come to feel comfortable in doing so, then there are certain essential conditions we must follow. We must get consent: 'I would like to place my hands gently on you as I pray. Is that okay?' As there is no specific healing effect, it does not matter where we place our hands, except of course that we must avoid placing them anywhere remotely improper! I usually put one hand lightly on the person's head and the other on their shoulder. There is certainly no necessity to place hands on the affected area, though it might not be inappropriate to do so, depending whereabouts on the anatomy it is. In a church context there will probably be other witnesses present. Even so, we should beware not just a perception of improper touch but also the potential for accusations of it. If in doubt, do not lay hands on people.

How should we pray in the health professions context?

Prayer for healing is a very simple matter. It involves coming in faith to a gracious God to ask him to touch the one in need. We have already noted Bishop Morris Maddocks' definition of Christian healing: 'Jesus Christ meeting you at the point of your need'. In principle we need do no more than remind God of the words used by the messengers who came to Jesus with news about Lazarus: 'Lord, the one you love is sick' (John 11:3). Prayer for healing can take place anywhere and at any time. While it should always be considered and conducted responsibly, we do not need necessarily to make a big deal about prayer for healing. It does not need to be confined to church services or to formal visitation by church leaders.

Christian doctors, nurses and other health professionals may therefore sometimes be led to offer prayer to patients. They may find this hard intellectually, not least in that they will not usually have an exact diagnosis. But we do not need an exact diagnosis in order to pray – God knows the diagnosis and knows what he wants to do!

Of course, Christian health professionals may invite patients to some formal healing activity in a church, but this will often be impossible or inappropriate. They may offer prayer for healing there and then. Professional regulatory bodies should not proscribe this but of course it must be done with extreme sensitivity. Prayer in the health professions context should build on the principles we derived from the study of James chapter five. It should involve:

- **clear change of role**
  To avoid the suggestion that what we are proposing is an accepted and standard National Health Service therapy – sadly it isn't – I believe that Christian health professionals should change role: 'Can I stop speaking to you as your doctor for a minute? I think you know that I am a committed Christian and I believe God wants to help you as you face this new treatment. I'd like to pray with you just for a moment. How do you feel about that?'

- **consent of the patient**
  Using such a preamble for ten years in general practice, and praying probably on average once a week for a patient, I only came across one patient who declined. I prayed for her in her

absence as soon as she left. This raises an interesting, if academic, hard question. Was my praying for her in some sense an assault in that she did not consent? However, we need to be particularly alert and ask ourselves, 'Could my patient comfortably refuse?' Doctors have enormous power over patients who might not feel able easily to disagree about something they do not really want.

- **fully informed consent of the patient**
  Consent is not valid ethically or in law unless it is fully informed. The patient should within reason know everything about what is going to happen and why. We should give a short and simple explanation about what prayer is. There should be a short discussion of what God may and may not do and every opportunity to refuse.

- **reassurance that we are not only praying in desperation**
  Several decades ago (when the culture in Britain was more familiar with Christianity than it is now), a Christian surgeon used to visit all his patients the night before their operations, offering to pray for them. One patient is reported to have replied: 'Gosh, doc, I hadn't realised I was as bad as that!' He clearly viewed the offer as the equivalent of Extreme Unction; as a consequence of his misunderstanding, he was frightened further.

- **no touch**
  I have already indicated that the laying on of hands in a pastoral context where others are present is an optional extra. Yet because doctors and nurses use their hands for specifically therapeutic purposes, despite our explanations, the potential for misunderstanding may be present. So I think touch while praying in a health professions context is always inappropriate. In chapter ten I recounted at length how I once prayed for a lady with severe headache and possible spiritual oppression. I carefully sat right across the room from her.

- **return to role before the consultation ends**
  Just as I think we should change role in order to pray with patients, so we should change back into medical mode before they leave. This is what they expect and deserve. They have come to see a doctor. We must make all of our contact respectful and patient centred, including the exceptional offer of prayer.

Are some conditions too trivial for prayer?

I do not want to exaggerate or over-emphasise my own experience of praying for healing, either in pastoral or occasionally in clinical circumstances. Still, I have come across a reluctance to ask for prayer by some Christians who generally believe in the concept of prayer for healing. Their reluctance to ask for or accept prayer is because they perceive their problem is too trivial.

I think this must be the spiritual equivalent of the Sorry-to-bother-you-doctor syndrome! I don't think Sorry-to-bother-you-God applies. He loves us and cares for every part of us. Jesus tells us, 'Even the very hairs of your head are all numbered' (Matthew 10:30 and Luke 12:7).

I sometimes used to reassure apologetic patients that the medical definition of trivia is 'something that happens to other people'. In other words, it's not trivial if it is happening to me. I believe God looks at it like that too. I have often prayed for relief of a sore throat before a speaking commitment so that I can maintain my voice for as long as I need it; those prayers have been answered. On the other hand, I have usually felt guilty about praying for the symptoms of the common cold and I would not hesitate to take appropriate medication as well. As always, it's not a case of pills or prayer but a case of pills and prayer.

A few years ago my wife and I were flying back from holiday when our plane was seriously delayed. We spent the whole night at the airport and then, to make matters worse, I developed unpleasant diarrhoea, having to visit the toilet every twenty minutes or so. Suddenly our plane was ready for boarding but I was still having frequent loose stools. I sat on the toilet seat and resolved to pray and lay hands on my own abdomen, summoning up all the faith I had. The diarrhoea stopped there and then and I flew comfortably back home. I had a normal stool a day or so later.

Was the diarrhoeal disease over before I prayed or did God graciously answer a prayer for healing? Archbishop William Temple, founder in the 1940s of the now defunct Churches Council for Health and Healing, used to say: 'When I pray, things happen, but people tell me it's just a coincidence. I don't know. But I do know that when I stop praying, the coincidences stop happening'.

Are some conditions too serious for prayer?

Conversely, I have come across Christians who believe generally in prayer for healing but who nevertheless seem to see a middle range of seriousness of conditions within which it is appropriate to pray. They will not go beyond that to pray for the life threatening. I vividly recall a friend with a strong Christian faith who died about twenty years ago from motor neurone disease. One day when I was visiting him at home, some time before the end of his life, I asked him carefully if he had ever considered prayer for healing. 'Oh no,' came his reply. 'I knew what motor neurone disease meant'. I said no more. I hope I didn't judge him then, nor do so now. That was his choice and it was right that he was the centre of his own disease and its management.

But I do think that, just as nothing is too small to bring to God – 'And even the very hairs of your head are all numbered', so nothing should be too large either – '"For nothing is impossible with God"' (Matthew 10:30 and Luke 1:37).

Is there a place for discerning how to pray?

The friend I have just mentioned may well have had some specific discernment from God that death from motor neurone disease was God's will for him, allowing him to concentrate on putting all his affairs in order and dying bravely and well.

1 Corinthians 2:14 talks of things that are spiritually discerned and the list of spiritual gifts in 1 Corinthians 12:8-10 includes the message of wisdom, the message of knowledge, the ability to distinguish between spirits and the interpretation of tongues. I am sure that some people have gifts of spiritual discernment and that proper use of such a gift would be very useful in knowing how to pray for healing.

What do we do if prayer for healing is not answered?

We saw in the previous chapter that God always answers prayer. Sometimes he does this with the green light of 'Go' and we receive exactly what we wanted, which in our context here is healing or at least cure. Sometimes he answers with the amber light of 'Wait' and we have to persist patiently in prayer. Sometimes he answers with the red light of 'Stop' and we do not get the longed for cure.

If we are to have a theology of healing to inspire the practice of Christian healing, we must also have a theology of suffering to help us to live when God doesn't grant a cure. We turn to the hard question, 'Why does God allow suffering?' in the next chapter.

References and Further Reading

Lawrence R. *The Practice of Christian Healing – A Guide for Beginners.* Downer's Grove, Illinois: IVP Saltshaker, 1996.
ISBN 0 8308 1960 6
The whole book is extremely practical. Chapter seven is titled *Anointing with Oil.*

Parker R, Fraser D and Rivers D. *In Search of Wholeness – a Christian theology of healing and practical training for church and medical settings.* Nottingham: St John's Extension Studies/Acorn Christian Foundation, 2000
ISBN 1 900920 09 3
This training manual synthesises theory and practice in a balanced way.

13

Why does God allow suffering?

The last chapter encouraged us to pray for healing. There will often be a positive response. This may be a thrilling tale of the unexpected or something even more significant and wonderful. Some may even see Category 1 miracles like those described in the New Testament. But often when we pray for healing, the person we pray for is not healed. They may feel no better and in fact the disappointment may make them feel worse than before. It is precisely because of the possibility of such disappointment that people being prayed for should give fully informed consent – facing the possibility that God may respond with the red light of 'No, it is not my purpose and one day you will understand', or the amber light of 'Wait, not yet', rather than the longed-for green light of 'Yes, go'. How then are we to understand their continued suffering? Come to that, how are we to understand suffering at all?

What is the philosophical problem?

We saw back in chapter one, *What is the Christian worldview?* that after a coherent presentation of the Christian faith, certain questions inevitably follow. One of these, whether there are only seven deadly questions or a few more than that, is always about suffering.

Suffering presents an intellectual problem for all of us, but particularly for Christians. An opponent might put it like this: 'You say God is all-knowing, all-loving and all-powerful? So why does he allow suffering?'

- Doesn't he know?
- Doesn't he care?
- Or can't he do anything about it?

I will attempt to respond to this philosophical problem in the theological discussion below, together with some comments from my own experience and the experience of others. But before that, we need to acknowledge another perhaps greater problem.

What is the pastoral problem?

The problem of suffering is not just philosophical and/or theological. Sooner or later we will all face pain and suffering – in patients, in loved ones, in ourselves. Where is God when it hurts? The reality of this question when it strikes, as sooner or later it will strike all of us, can damage the faith of the strongest Christian, and even cause some to appear to lose their faith.

This chapter aims to provide a biblical framework so we can understand suffering, so we can argue the Christian case to others, and so that we ourselves can find God's help in times of need.

What does Christian theology say?

Against the background outlined in chapter one of what it is that Christians believe, and bearing in mind that there will always be limits to what we can understand, we can consider a theological account of suffering under five headings:

- **freewill**

  God allows us freedom of choice and the wrong choices we make damage ourselves and damage others. Possibly 90 percent of suffering in the world is directly due to man's sin. Is God to blame when a drunk driver kills half a dozen children at a bus stop? Is God to blame when the rich world maintains its selfish standard of living by prolonging poverty in the greater part of the world, with all the attendant consequences for health and longevity? We considered the links between sin and sickness and death in chapter nine, and there is no doubt that the irresponsible exercise of freewill, which is effectively what sin is, causes most of the suffering in the world.

- **fall**

  The other ten percent of suffering in the world is indirectly due to sin through its corrupting effect on the way the world is. As Paul puts it: 'We know that the whole creation has been groaning as in the pains of childbirth right up to the present time' (Romans 8:22). The wrong choices of Eve and Adam, and the wrong choices of each and every one of us since have damaged the whole creation. Suffering and sickness are part of the warp and woof of life for everyone.

- **faith**

  If there were a God who cared, the obvious question to shout would be: 'Why doesn't God do something about suffering?' The Christian answer is that he has – in Jesus. The healing in the atonement debate is a difficult one (see chapter five) but Jesus not only died for our sins on the cross but took up our infirmities and carried our sorrows (Isaiah 53:4). 'For we do not have a high priest who is unable to sympathise with our weaknesses, but we have one who has been tempted in every way, just as we are – yet was without sin' (Hebrews 4:15). Jesus hurts for us; Jesus hurts with us. The challenging question to Christians in the face of suffering is: 'How can I bring Jesus into this situation?'

Without being too simplistic, Christian health professionals and lay Christians involved in the healing ministry are bringing Jesus into the situation just by being there. Patients are often overwhelmed with all the activity and noise going on around them, and a simple presence or a silent listener can be very healing. This was well put by the patient who paraphrased the saying we might have expected with his exasperated expression: 'Don't just do something; stand there!'

• **future**

We have already seen in chapter two, *What does it mean to be human?* that the Book of Revelation prophesies a certain time:

> *Now the dwelling of God is with men, and he will live with them. They will be his people, and God himself will be with them and be their God. He will wipe every tear from their eyes. There will be no more death or mourning or crying or pain, for the old order of things has passed away. (Revelation 21:3-4)*

Let me be quite clear: suffering is a bad thing and we should do every legitimate thing we can to reduce it. By legitimate I mean that we are not allowed to break God's clear teaching elsewhere (the commandment 'You shall not murder' in Exodus 20:13 for example) in order to tidy up a problem like suffering. However we all know that on this earth we will never get rid of all suffering. Against that present reality, the eternal perspective of heaven sets the temporary sufferings of this present age in a somewhat different perspective. We must beware the truth in the pie-in-the-sky-when-you-die accusation, but belief in eternity is foundational for Christianity.

The real questions are: 'Do we Christians really believe this?' and 'Do we live our lives accordingly?' I will return to this subject in the next, final chapter.

• **finally**

God could solve the intellectual problem of suffering at a stroke, by performing euthanasia on all those who are suffering and by wiping out all those who cause it. But where would that leave you and me? In his mercy, God doesn't take this option!

What does the Book of Job teach us?

The Old Testament book of Job has lent itself to several sayings in everyday use – we sometimes say of someone longsuffering that he has the patience of Job, or we may describe unsympathetic friends as Job's comforters. But it is a long and difficult book, challenging us both intellectually and in our faith. Job is a model religious citizen who has been blessed with family and prosperity. God allows Satan to test him, in ways including threats to his health, in order to demonstrate to Satan that Job's real faith does not depend on what he personally gets out of it. The book describes an extreme case of a contest between Satan and God, though Job never knows this – he is not going through his suffering in a state of fully informed consent.

The comforters explain Job's suffering as caused by sin which he is either not aware of or will not acknowledge, but that is not the answer. Indeed Job never gets to know the answer, but the breakthrough point for him is when as a result of his directing hard questions to God he hears back from God and realises that he has been asking all the wrong questions. Glimpses of God's different perspective and the almost infinite mystery of suffering put him back on track. He confesses: 'Surely I spoke of things I did not understand, things too wonderful for me to know' (Job 42:3).

There is a happy ending for Job: '...the Lord made him prosperous again and gave him twice as much as he had before...the Lord blessed the latter part of Job's life more than the first' (Job 42:10, 12). Our sufferings may not on this earth have happy endings, but we can learn from Job both to have an accepting attitude and to ask the right questions, or at least to stop asking the wrong questions.

For example, the obvious question 'Why?' is not usually helpful. It could perhaps be countered philosophically with 'Why not?' If I had been born and raised in sub-Saharan Africa or at a different point in history then I might well have faced a great deal more suffering already. Rather, the more constructive questions to ask in the face of suffering are the 'Whats?' 'What do you want me to learn from all this, God? What do you want to show me? What does this mean for my marriage, family and career? What can I do to turn this into something positive for me and others?'

Such an approach, one of how am I going to go through this suffering, is very much easier said than done, but asking the right sorts of questions is one of the main lessons from the book of Job.

What do we do in practice?

The theological framework above – the glib five-points-beginning-with-F answer – is a theoretical one and may well be worse than useless for people who are in the throes of suffering. Remembering the great medical principle, first do no harm, and remembering the damage that Job's comforters did, we should not make the situation of people in pain worse. They almost certainly do not need theology or too many texts from the Bible. They may, for example, need a gentle arm around the shoulder and to be given permission to shout hard questions at God. Job did and astonishingly was commended by God as he rebuked the three friends: 'you have not spoken of me what is right, as my servant Job has' (Job 42:7).

So, how in practice do we deal with suffering professionally, pastorally, and personally?

How do we deal professionally with suffering?

It goes almost without saying that we do all we can medically, using our skills and training, to bring relief by legitimate means. I stress legitimate means because killing the patient as in abortion or euthanasia is not an option for the Christian. The hospice movement (which was initially Christian) and its derived specialty, palliative care, have taught all specialties a whole-person approach to relieving severe pain and other difficult aspects of human suffering.

We must remain objective and detached in professional practice, but we are human too and will have our own subjective responses. If we cease to 'mourn with those who mourn' (Romans 12:15) we may be in danger of burnout and of becoming bad doctors or nurses. Only twice in fourteen years of clinical practice did I come to weep for a patient. I later realised that coincidentally those two patients were the only two in my career where the issue of euthanasia came up. On the first occasion an inappropriate and unnecessary dose of opiates was suggested by a boss but not administered by me. The second time a patient in general practice with a tragic medical problem asked me repeatedly to kill him.

How do we deal pastorally with suffering?

Hospital chaplains are those most obviously tasked with this. Clergy and laity in local churches are increasingly having a role to play, and with a growing professional recognition of spirituality, there are opportunities in the community and in primary care for a role for health professionals that is more pastoral than professional. This role may simply be a case of 'Don't just do something; stand there!' As I described above, this is a simple presence.

I also mentioned a silent listener. Few of us are ever listened to enough, and there is a great danger of us not being listened to adequately when we are ill. As a GP I regularly heard patients describe their inpatient care by saying: 'Nobody ever listened to me properly'. I currently chair the Acorn Christian Foundation, and part of Acorn's role is to train lay people in structured Christian Listening. In the most basic introduction to this, Acorn trainers invite group participants to say how they feel when they are listened to properly and the sorts of words which come up include valued, special, important, loved, secure, worthwhile, wanted, safe and appreciated. I suggest that these are all healing words.

By contrast, the list of words from people when they are not listened to includes angry, frustrated, impotent, powerless, rejected, valueless, irritated, annoyed and worthless. These words not only reflect a failure to bring any healing, but may reflect further harm.

I suggested in chapter seven, *What are Christians doing today?* that part of the reason for the popularity of many complementary/alternative practitioners is that their listening contrasts so starkly with the perceived arrogance of the busy doctor. Lay Christian volunteers who are properly trained, properly supervised and accountable could have a very significant role to play in a pastoral response to suffering by providing Christian listening.

How do we deal personally with suffering?

I now describe three occasions of illness in my life and their relevance to the hard questions of suffering. My clinical experience is that when they are unwell, patients are primarily seeking two things (apart from getting better). They want a diagnosis, a label that lets them come to terms with what they have got. They also want to know how their problem fits in with who they are and what it will mean to them. I share a little of what I learnt from these three episodes with the hope that my accounts may help some professionally or personally.

Glandular fever – a consequence of sin?

> *Blessed is the man whom God corrects; so do not despise the discipline of the Almighty. For he wounds, but he also binds up; he injures, but his hands also heal. (Job 5:17-18)*

These words are spoken by Eliphaz, one of Job's comforters. Although we have already discovered that he was wrong to apply them to Job, the expressed sentiments are often true. I had never had anything more than the self-limiting or easily treated illnesses of childhood until I contracted infectious mononucleosis (glandular fever) in my last year at medical school. I was very familiar with the Bible's teaching that sex outside marriage is wrong, and had resolved never to go beyond a certain level of physical intimacy before marriage. However, after the woman who became my wife and I got engaged, I succumbed to temptation and, without giving details, on a number of occasions wilfully went too far. It was the most deliberate act of disobedience against God that I had committed in the couple of years since I had become a Christian.

A month or so later I began to feel unwell and the inevitable blood test confirmed glandular fever. Even though it is nicknamed the *kissing disease*, my fiancée never caught it. I was very sick for months with some extremely unpleasant symptoms and had barely recovered on our wedding day six months later.

Rightly or wrongly I have always seen that illness as a consequence of my sin of deliberately and repeatedly disobeying God. I learnt a spiritual lesson the hard way. Now, I do not think God sent an angel to infect me with glandular fever. Nor do I think he allowed Satan to inflict me with the demon of glandular fever – I do not think there is such a demon! But I can accept that my deliberate and repeated sin caused guilt that, together with tiredness, weakened my immune system so that, in turn, I was more likely to go down with a virus that is always prevalent in student communities.

In chapter three, *What is health?* I quoted Psalm 32:1-5 where David links physical and psychological ill health with sin he has not previously confessed. We read of the link between unconfessed sin, depression and possible physical symptoms again in Psalm 51. David wrote this after Nathan the prophet convicted him of his sin in his adultery with Bathsheba:

> *Cleanse me with hyssop, and I shall be clean; wash me, and I shall be whiter than snow. Let me hear joy and gladness; let the bones you have crushed rejoice. Hide your face from my sins and blot out all my iniquity. Create in me a pure heart, O God, and renew a steadfast spirit within me. Do not cast me from your presence or take your Holy Spirit from me. Restore to me the joy of your salvation and grant me a willing spirit, to sustain me. (Psalm 51:7-12)*

Appendicitis – time off to complete my first book?

And we know that in all things God works for the good of those who love him, who have been called according to his purpose. (Romans 8:28)

These words are often misunderstood and quoted glibly by Christians to reassure themselves that God is in control when, in their heart of hearts, they are not sure he is. Still, it is true that God is always working for good, even when it is not initially apparent.

In the late summer of 1987 I devoted two weeks of my annual holiday to researching a book on the 50th anniversary of the Brook Lane Medical Mission for which I was working at the time – see chapter six, *What has the church done historically?* We wanted to get the book out as soon as possible to coincide with the anniversary. I was the only one likely to write it but the research had taken longer than I expected. By the end of my two weeks off, I had only written the first chapter. To make matters worse, a partner had just left and the remaining two of us knew that we would be struggling temporarily to do the work of three. I had no idea how I was going to finish the book.

As I worked on the first chapter, I felt a bit light headed but assumed it was just artistic inspiration. As I laid down my pen at the end of the draft and rose from my desk, an acute pain hit me in my right iliac fossa. I said to myself, 'You've got appendicitis!' Three hours later with a fever and constant right iliac fossa pain, I called in my GP. I was admitted to hospital and a moderately inflamed appendix was removed. I came home five days later; during two weeks' convalescence before going back to the practice, I finished the book.

My partners had to find a locum in a hurry and, in fact, she stayed for the next fifteen years. I discovered again I was not indispensable, and the book later came out and helped recruitment to the Mission. Rightly or wrongly, I have always viewed that surgical episode as an example of a Romans 8:28 situation.

Neuropathy – the thorn in my flesh?

To keep me from becoming conceited because of these surpassingly great revelations, there was given me a thorn in my flesh, a messenger of Satan, to torment me. Three times I pleaded with the Lord to take it away from me. But he said to me, "My grace is sufficient for you, for my power is made perfect in weakness." Therefore I will boast all the more gladly about my weaknesses, so that Christ's power may rest on me. (2 Corinthians 12:7-9)

We considered this passage in chapter five, *What does the Bible say?* and concluded that while it may not necessarily be about physical illness, Paul's (surely deliberate) vagueness does not exclude that interpretation. Does God leave some people with chronic painful ailments because those individuals need a continuing reminder about their need for dependence on God?

Following my bout of appendicitis, I thought for the first time in my life about my own mortality. Having two young children, I thought I ought to leave them better provided for in the event of untimely death, so I bumped up my insurance cover considerably. I had to have a comprehensive top to toe medical examination, which I passed. A little later God called me out of general practice, and I was appointed as Assistant General Secretary of the Christian Medical Fellowship. At the interview I was asked whether I was in good health, and was able to reply honestly that to the best of my knowledge and belief I was.

Six months went by. I loved my new job, but was vaguely aware of having less physical drive than before and of slowing down. Then one weekend, I suddenly developed widespread fasciculation, irregular movements of many of my muscles. I had noticed this in the bath occasionally for a couple of years but had been ignoring it, because healthy people occasionally get such a sign and because the commonest disease by far which has it as a diagnostic feature is motor neurone disease. This is pretty near the top of most doctors' lists of diseases *not* to have.

But there was no ignoring this. I got my books out and did the fastest ever neurology revision course. I also went over my reflexes with a patella hammer – nothing in the legs. Within an hour I had made a tentative diagnosis of motor neurone disease, as I thought I had purely motor signs and symptoms.

Just over a week later a professor of neurology did not disagree with that diagnosis, though pointed out there were more tests to be done. It was a couple of weeks later still before comprehensive nerve conduction studies demonstrated a significant abnormality in my sensory nerves too, of which I had not been aware. This meant that I could not possibly have motor neurone disease. I should of course have been delighted even as I lay wired up on the couch. Ironically, I wasn't in fact delighted at first. By then I had spent three interesting weeks coming to terms with dying unpleasantly within a year or so.

Many more tests followed and by exclusion I gained a diagnosis that seems to have another word added to it every time I attend hospital: currently it is chronic idiopathic axonal motor sensory neuropathy. All that was fifteen years ago. I have a number of different symptoms which progress slowly and they could perhaps be described as my thorn in the flesh.

I have received prayer many times and in many different ways, but there has never been any sign of the least response physically. Instead I am given grace to manage practical difficulties and have become, I think, a more whole person despite, or because of, my physical problems. Perhaps God's power has been made perfect in my weakness.

I share aspects of these three medical problems of mine with diffidence. I do not believe anecdotes have much power to make objective points, but I hope they may give some readers insights to help professionally or perhaps personally. Perhaps it may give someone permission to share their own story, be it a good news story or not, so that, in Paul's words, '…we can comfort those in any trouble with the comfort we ourselves have received from God' (2 Corinthians 1:4).

Can good come out of suffering?

Church tradition has tended to make much of the redemptive benefit of suffering. I stick with my statement that suffering is a bad thing and we should do everything legitimate within our power to remove or reduce it. However, there is no doubt that in facing suffering we can be helped in our faith. Paul writes: '…we also rejoice in our sufferings, because we know that suffering produces perseverance; perseverance, character; and character, hope. And hope does not disappoint us, because God has poured out his love into our hearts by the Holy Spirit, whom he has given us'. (Romans 5:3-5)

In the context of wanting to be like his Lord, Paul also writes: 'I want to know Christ and the power of his resurrection and the fellowship of sharing in his sufferings, becoming like him in his death' (Philippians 3:10). Perhaps the hymn writer William Cowper (1731-1800) knew something of that mystery of 'the fellowship of sharing in his sufferings'. He endured bouts of severe depression, but we might not have had his great hymns had depression not been his particular thorn in the flesh. One of his classics begins 'God moves in a mysterious way, His wonders to perform'. There is always mystery, but it has been my experience that good things are always happening at the same time as, and in association with, bad things. I do not think I can recall a single clinical case in fourteen years' frontline medicine where that was not so somehow or other.

I recall, for example, a family where father had died at home from lung cancer. One of the daughters said to me: 'It's sad doctor, dad dying the way he did. I suppose it was the smoking. But do you know, something really good happened. The family had been at loggerheads for years, and some of us weren't even talking to each other. But when dad was dying we decided we had to present a united front around his bedside. So we all started talking again and, do you know, we haven't stopped since.' God indeed moves in a mysterious way. *Every cloud has a silver lining* or *it's an ill wind that blows nobody any good* may be everyday folklore expressions hinting at the same concept.

I mentioned in the last chapter that it is often when people are ill that they have time to think about life and its meaning, perhaps for the first time ever. C S Lewis emphasised this with his comment in *The Problem of Pain*, 'God whispers to us in our pleasures, speaks in our conscience, but shouts in our pains; it is his megaphone to rouse a deaf world'.

And finally?

The success of modern medical science has deluded us into thinking we can know everything, but there are aspects of suffering in general and the suffering of individuals in particular that will always remain a mystery. We should beware letting that acknowledgement become a cop out, but we do have to live with mystery. Suffering is a mystery we all have to live with, and although we should respond to it with the best medical care we can, we would do well also to live by the truth in the anonymous saying, 'Suffering is not a question that demands an answer; it is not a problem that demands a solution; it is a mystery that demands a presence'.

References and Further Reading

Carson D A. *How long, O Lord? Reflections on suffering and evil.* Leicester: IVP, 1991
ISBN 0 85110 950 0
This is a comprehensive theological and pastoral consideration.

Davies G. *Genius and Grace*. London: Hodder and Stoughton, 1992
ISBN 0 340 56572 1
Chapter three is titled *Darkness into Light* and considers the life of William Cowper.

Lewis C S. *The Problem of Pain*. London: Fount, 1998
ISBN 0 0062 8093 5
This classic work on suffering has recently been reissued.

14

Do Christians really believe in heaven?

This book has used the Bible as the source for ideas for our health needs and for our National Health Service. These would be transformational if implemented. We have tried to interpret the Bible correctly by referring back to four theological pillars: creation, fall, redemption, and future hope. At different points in the book we have examined the significance of the first three pillars, but hardly so far considered the fourth. The last of these pillars, future hope, is not a timid afterthought but should influence the way we live now.

What is the Christian's future hope?

We considered the Christian worldview according to five propositions. The fourth of these was titled *What if I do?* and was about a positive personal response to the offer of Christ:

> *If I respond by turning away from the wrong way of living, by thanking God that the penalty for my wrong choices has been met by Christ's death on the cross, by acknowledging that God has confirmed his power in raising Jesus from the dead, and by committing myself from now on to living for Christ, then I know a new life.*
>
> *I know new life here on earth, both naturally through the deep sense of peace that comes from realising God's forgiveness, and supernaturally through God's presence as he comes to live within me through his Holy Spirit. I will know that new life in heaven and can be certain of being with God eternally when I die, not because of what I have done but because of my faith in what Jesus has done.*

What do we know of heaven?

This proposition has briefly introduced the concept of heaven as an eternal reward for true faith in Christ and a life lived accordingly. The Christian believer can be certain of the reality of heaven, even if we know little of the detail. Much is mystery but Paul reveals something of God's master plan to restore the cosmos to himself:

> *And he made known to us the mystery of his will according to his good pleasure, which he purposed in Christ, to be put into effect when the times will have reached their fulfilment – to bring all things in heaven and on earth together under one head, even Christ. (Ephesians 1:9-10)*

Creation is to be redeemed and God's people will be in his presence forever. There will be nothing of sin or the devil there. We will have a resurrection body, in contrast to the natural body:

> *'The body that is sown is perishable, it is raised imperishable; it is sown in dishonour, it is raised in glory; it is sown in weakness, it is raised in power; it is sown a natural body, it is raised a spiritual body' (1 Corinthians 15:42-44).*

Paul goes on to contrast 'the first man' with 'the second man': 'The first man was of the dust of the earth, the second man from heaven' (1 Corinthians 15:47). In his second letter to the Christians at Corinth, he uses a favourite metaphor of mine, the contrast between the temporary tent of the earthly body and our eternal house in heaven:

> *Now we know that if the earthly tent we live in is destroyed, we have a building from God, an eternal house in heaven, not built by human hands. Meanwhile we groan, longing to be clothed with our heavenly dwelling, because when we are clothed, we will not be found naked. For while we are in this tent, we groan and are burdened, because we do not wish to be unclothed but to be clothed with our heavenly dwelling, so that what is mortal may be swallowed up by life. Now it is God who has made us for this very purpose and has given us the Spirit as a deposit, guaranteeing what is to come. (2 Corinthians 5:1-5)*

The prophecy of Revelation tells us: 'Now the dwelling of God is with men, and he will live with them. They will be his people, and God himself will be with them and be their God. He will wipe every tear from their eyes. There will be no more death or mourning or crying or pain, for the old order of things has passed away' (Revelation 21:3-4). In our consideration of suffering we decided that, if this is true, eternity sets our earthly sufferings, however bad they are, into a different perspective.

What do we know of hell?

Before moving on to consider whether most western Christians live their lives as if heaven as described were truly real, we need to remember the fifth and final proposition, *What if I don't?* It ran as follows:

> *The fifth and final proposition concerns the individual who responds negatively. If I ignore God, either passively and apathetically, or in active rebellion and rejection, then by my own choice I will not know that new life now on earth either naturally or supernaturally. If I continue to ignore God up to the end of my life then one day God will have to say, 'I'm sorry, I don't know you. You didn't want to know me. I can't let you into my heaven.' I will forever be separated from God in hell.*

In hell there is nothing of God. Even his common grace is completely absent. Common grace is the theological term for the fact that on earth God's creation blessings are available to all irrespective of where they stand before him: 'He causes his sun to rise on the evil and the good, and sends rain on the righteous and the unrighteous' (Matthew 5:45). Similarly, common grace means there is some good in all – or almost all – of us. Indeed some people who are not Christian believers live more loving lives than many who are.

To spend eternity in the absence of everything of God, and with others whose selfishness now knows no checks and whose evil is unrestrained, is the spiritual reality of hell. In the medical context, ethics require us to warn individuals and society at large of the adverse health consequences of their choices. Unpopular and unfashionable though it may be, Christians have to warn individuals and society at large of the adverse consequences of a choice against Christ.

So, do Christians really believe in heaven?

The reality of heaven should set the difficulties of this present age into a different perspective. Of course we have an absolute obligation to treat disease and reduce suffering, but we do need to remember at all times that this earth is not all there is. Indeed, C S Lewis uses his beautiful word *Shadowlands* in his Narnia Chronicles for the Christian belief that this earth is not the real world, but a shadow of the real substantial world to come. If all Christians really believed that and lived their lives accordingly, it would surely change the way we live now.

In the 1990s my specialist subject became, through no choice of my own, euthanasia. I have spoken to Christians of all denominations all over the UK and further afield about euthanasia, assisted suicide and related matters of life and death. Some of the platform discussions and, even more, the private conversations after meetings have been very revealing. I have discovered that most Christians, whilst knowing about heaven in their heads as a theological concept, do not really believe in the reality of it in their heart of hearts.

The church is always more affected by the culture around it than it affects that culture. The western church is materialistic, hedonistic and self-centred, and I speak to myself first and foremost. We expect instant relief and gratification. Hence all pain and suffering must be removed immediately, and we must permanently be pampered and pleasured. If we really believed in our heart of hearts in the reality of heaven, wouldn't our health expectations be different? If we really believed in our heart of hearts in the reality of heaven, wouldn't our economic behaviour be different? Wouldn't our whole lives be different?

Death is a junction, not a terminus. At death Christians go to be with their Lord for ever. We fall asleep and wake in the presence of Christ. This is in fact the ultimate healing! Unless Christ comes back first, there is for each of us '…a time to die' (Ecclesiastes 3:2). Probably my most helpful contribution to the bioethics debates about euthanasia and related subjects has been to get the expression, 'Life has a natural end' into the consciousness of ethicists and health professionals.

Why is there a taboo on discussing death and dying?

Christian faith lived out to the full here in the Shadowlands must point people towards heaven. It must help break the taboo on the discussion of death and dying that bedevils ethical debate and health service planning and is part of the satanic strategy to keep us thinking on a material plane at all times, pretending that we will never die, and spending some health resources inappropriately.

There is a taboo in the health services about discussing death and dying. We may have moved on from the days only a decade or two ago when patients discovered their illness was terminal because the ward round no longer stopped at their bed, but many doctors still avoid recognising the approaching reality. Perhaps they can only see death as a failure. Maybe the death of their patient would spoil their research trial figures. Perhaps they simply do not know how to talk about death. Could their patient's approaching death force them to face their own mortality?

I am convinced that we all need to get real about death and dying. Without sacrificing one iota of the high-tech care we have been blessed with, we need the discernment to use that healthcare on those who will benefit from it. We need to do something much more effective about the huge disparities in health provision between rich and poor. Without moving one inch towards the euthanasia position, we need to abandon meddlesome medicine that only prolongs the inevitable. Sometimes death needs to be welcomed as the portal to final and full healing.

Experience from the hospice movement shows that such a Christian approach meets the felt needs of patients and their families and squares with their intuitions. The enormous secular support for hospices and palliative care should reassure us and reinforce our conviction that we are right in the way we approach death and dying. Let us have more confidence in what we believe!

The last word?

The Christian Medical Fellowship's best selling book is James Casson's posthumously published *Dying – the greatest adventure of my life*. A young family doctor, he died of a malignancy in 1980 after a long illness. He recorded many of the lessons he learned during that difficult process. He describes the outcomes of various prayers for healing. He was not cured and struggled with this, and with his feelings about how to pray and be prayed for. He ends:

> *However, the conflict of whether 'I was doing everything correctly' did trouble me. Release came with the realisation that the whole issue was out of my hands. One morning I had a clear picture that I was in a boat. Before, when asking for healing, it was as though I was in a punt where one stands at one end pushing on the punt pole and steering with more or less expertise. Afterwards, I was in a rowing boat, my back to the direction I was going, but travelling in a much more leisurely fashion. The great joy was that the Lord was at the tiller, his face gently smiling and his eyes twinkling as he quietly guided me to my destination.*
>
> *Was I healed? Yes I believe I was.*

References and Further Reading

Casson JH. *Dying – the greatest adventure of my life*.
Republished with Casson P. *My Cancer*. London: Christian Medical Fellowship, 1999
ISBN 0 906747 32 5

Appendices

Appendix 1.
Healing miracles in the Old Testament

Sarah's conception – Genesis 17:15-19, 18:10-15, 21:1-8

Moses' hand made leprous and restored – Exodus 4:6-7 (see page 54)

Viewing the bronze snake healing those with snakebite – Numbers 21:4-9, 2 Kings 18:4, John 3:14, 1 Corinthians 10:9

Elijah raising the widow's son from death – 1 Kings 17:17-24

Elisha raising the Shunammite's son from death – 2 Kings 4:17-37

Elisha's command healing Naaman of leprosy – 2 Kings 5:1-19

A dead man revived through touching Elisha's bones – 2 Kings 13:21

Hezekiah healed (prayer and a fig poultice) – 2 Kings 20:1-11, 2 Chronicles 32:24, Isaiah 38

Appendix 2.
Jesus' miracles of healing individuals

An official's son close to death – John 4:46-54

A man possessed by an evil spirit – Mark 1:23-28, Luke 4:33-37

Peter's mother-in-law lying in bed with a fever – Matthew 8:14-15, Mark 1:29-31, Luke 4:38-39

A man with leprosy – Matthew 8:2-4 (see page 75), Mark 1: 40-45 (see page 58), Luke 5: 12-15

A paralytic – Matthew 9:2-8, Mark 2:3-12, Luke 5:18-26 (see page 125)

An invalid at the pool of Bethesda – John 5:2-15

A man with a shrivelled hand – Matthew 12:9-14 (see page 56), Mark 3:1-6, Luke 6:6-11

A centurion's paralysed servant – Matthew 8:5-13 (see page 125), Luke 7:2-10 (see page 125)

A widow's son raised from death – Luke 7:11-17 (see page 58)

Two demon-possessed men – Matthew 8:28-34, Mark 5:1-20 (see page 115), Luke 8:26-39

A woman subject to bleeding for twelve years – Matthew 9:20-22, Mark 5:25-34 (see page 123), Luke 8:43-48

Jairus' daughter raised from death – Matthew 9:18-26 (see page 127), Mark 5:21-43 (see page 124), Luke 8:40-56

Two blind men – Matthew 9:27-31

A man who was demon-possessed and could not talk – Matthew 9:32-34

A Canaanite woman's daughter with demon-possession – Matthew 15:21-28, Mark 7:24-30 (see page 116)

A man who was deaf and could hardly talk – Mark 7:32-37

A blind man at Bethsaida – Mark 8:22-26 (see page 56)

A boy with epilepsy/an evil spirit – Matthew 17:14-21 (see page 129), Mark 9:14-29 (see page 116), Luke 9:37-43

A man blind from birth – John 9:1-41 (see pages – 106-107)

A demon-possessed man who was blind and dumb – Matthew 12:22-29 (see page 59), Luke 11:14-26

A woman crippled by a spirit for eighteen years – Luke 13:10-17

A man suffering from dropsy – Luke 14:1-6

Lazarus raised from death – John 11:1-44 (see page 140)

One (or two) blind men – Matthew 20:29-34, Mark 10:46-52, Luke 18:35-43

The servant's severed ear – Luke 22:50-51

Appendix 3.
Jesus' miracles of healing groups and crowds

At Peter's house: *'many who were demon-possessed were brought to him, and he drove out the spirits with a word, and healed all the sick'* – Matthew 8:16 (see page 57), Mark 1:32-34, Luke 4:40-41 (see page 139)

Throughout Galilee: *'preaching in their synagogues and driving out demons'* – Mark 1:39

Crowds: *'Many followed him, and he healed all their sick'* – Matthew 12:15, Mark 3:10

Nazareth: *'he did not do many miracles there'* – Matthew 13:58, Mark 6:5-6 (see page 127)

Ten men who had leprosy: *'And as they went, they were cleansed'* – Luke 17:11-19 (see page 48)

Gennesaret: *'all who touched him were healed'* – Matthew 14:34-36, Mark 6:53-56

Galilee/Syria: *'healing every disease and sickness among the people . . . those suffering severe pain, the demon-possessed, the epileptics and the paralytics'* – Matthew 4:23-24 (see page 59), Luke 6:17-19

Through all the towns and villages: *'healing every disease and sickness'* – Matthew 9:35 (see page 59)

After John the Baptist's question: *'the blind receive sight, the lame walk, those who have leprosy are cured, the deaf hear, the dead are raised'* – Matthew 11:4-5 (see page 58), Luke 7:21-22

Before the feeding of the 5,000: *'he had compassion on them and healed their sick'* – Matthew 14:14 (see page 58), Luke 9:11, John 6:2

Along the Sea of Galilee: *'the lame, the blind, the crippled, the dumb and many others'* – Matthew 15:30

Judea: *'large crowds followed him, and he healed them there'* – Matthew 19:2

Crowds of people: *'to be healed of their sicknesses'* – Luke 5:15

After Herod's threat: *'I will drive out demons and heal people today and tomorrow'* – Luke 13:32

At the temple: *'The blind and the lame came to him . . . and he healed them'* – Matthew 21:14

Peter's description of Jesus: *'he went around doing good and healing all who were under the power of the devil'* – Acts 10:38

Appendix 4.
Healings performed through the apostles and other disciples

4.1 In the Gospels
The Twelve given authority and sent – Matthew 10:1-8 (see page 61), Mark 6:7-13 (see page 62), Luke 9:1-6 (see page 62)

The seventy-two appointed and sent – Luke 10:1-20 (see page 62)

4.2 In Acts – Healing of individuals
A man crippled from birth at the temple gate – Acts 3:1-10

Paul's sight restored – Acts 9:10-19, 22:11-13

Aeneas, a paralytic bedridden for eight years – Acts 9:32-35

Tabitha raised from the dead – Acts 9:36-42

A man in Lystra lame from birth – Acts 14:8-18 (see page 123)

A slave girl with a spirit by which she predicted the future – Acts 16:16-18

Eutychus raised from the dead – Acts 20:7-12

Paul healed from snakebite – Acts 28:3-6

Publius' father with fever and dysentery – Acts 28:8

4.3 In Acts – Healing of groups
After Pentecost: *'many wonders and miraculous signs'* – Acts 2:43

On the streets: *'so that at least Peter's shadow might fall on some of them…bringing their sick and those tormented by evil spirits, and all of them were healed'* – Acts 5:12-16 (see page 63)

Stephen: *'great wonders and miraculous signs'* – Acts 6:8

Philip: *'evil spirits came out of many, and many paralytics and cripples were healed'* – Acts 8:5-8

Paul and Barnabas: *'miraculous signs and wonders'* – Acts 14:3

Paul: *'extraordinary miracles . . . Handkerchiefs and aprons that had touched him were taken to the sick, and their illnesses were cured and the evil spirits left them'* – Acts 19:11-12 (see page 63)

Malta: *'the rest of the sick on the island came and were cured'* – Acts 28:9

Index